LIKE IT MATTERS

An Unpublishable Novel

Lee Klein

Sagging
Meniscus

Set in Mrs Eaves with LaTeX.

ISBN: 978-1-952386-87-9 (paperback)
ISBN: 978-1-952386-88-6 (ebook)
Library of Congress Control Number: 2023952261

Sagging Meniscus Press
Montclair, New Jersey
saggingmeniscus.com

"When asked how I write, I like to say *like it matters*."
—Jonathan David Grooms

Like It Matters

I.

Yes, I said yes, I will yes, I responded before I marked the date months in advance on my calendar at work. I had looked forward to it all winter and spring but once the day came I decided to stay home and write. My wife figured something must be wrong with me. I'd even said, she said, quoting me, mocking me, that I was "so psyched for this year's Bloomsday."

I had looked forward to it for too long, and the laws of literary fiction state that all those who look forward to the future, instead of acting in the present or thinking about the past, shall be punished. Knowing I was due for a smackdown I thought it best to stay home and work as everyone else went out and got wasted. So much better, even on the most beautiful Saturday, a gift from the gods, barometric perfection, deep blue sky crossed with feathery clouds. Knowing writer friends plus the great Jonathan David Grooms would spend the night drinking and the next day nursing self-inflicted head wounds I'd get to bed early and wake at dawn to ensure the embryonic novel manuscript I'm working on develops into something viable.

I want to be there of course but I also want to *not* be there. I want to have the discipline to deny myself the big night capped by the arrival of the important writer from out of town. I want to spend those hours pushing the little creative offspring I've been nurturing further into existence, nudging it from simple viability toward something resembling inarguable excellence.

That's all I want: the ability to resist temptation, especially to socialize, and instead produce undeniable excellence. I want to sit at home and work while all my area writer friends and the most famous youngish writer of literary fiction in the United States, if not the most famous youngish writer of literary fiction in the entire world, descend on a favorite neighborhood bar. I want to take advantage of the time they spend drinking and talking and the next day recovering, putting themselves together after the blowout. I want to take advantage of Saturday night and the following morning to produce *undeniable excellence* while they don't write a word. I want to make the most of my life, and if making the most of life means staying home and working while everyone talks and drinks and recovers from talking and drinking, so be it.

II.

I spent the morning with super-pregnant wife arranging books on new bookshelves and then taking one book on a long walk-and-read session. Everything seemed in the right spot, rounding into form, so why worry about meeting friends later? I didn't have to talk to Grooms. I could sit as far from him as possible. Or I could slip to the bathroom if seated near him, bum cigarettes outside until I was sure my seat was claimed. The whole night I expected competition for his interest, for a connection that might become correspondence and opportunities that otherwise wouldn't exist.

The least established of my writer friends, I'm always ready to talk about what people are reading. I've heard of everything because I worked at a used bookstore in my twenties but also because I never attended graduate school or taught university-level classes. Instead of reading student stories and teaching stories I assigned to students, I've spent the years since it was clear I was a writer reading as much as I could, novels more than stories since there's something about the commitment the novel requires, the freedom to explore its space, that invigorates my spirit. So, because I'm at least familiar with everything, I perceive my reputation among writer reader friends as better than my limited publication record.

I've only published stories and reviews on a weird little literary website back when I lived in Brooklyn before I moved to Philadelphia. I couldn't afford to live any longer in Greenpoint so I moved to an inexpensive city that left me alone to work, where I met my wife and wrote three novels over the past seven years. The first two I have not been able to publish whereas the most recently completed novel manuscript, my third since moving to Philadelphia, I have some hope for, although I know having hope goes against the laws of literary fiction. To guard against having hope for the most recent novel manuscript, I've been working on something new, *a fourth novel* since moving to Philadelphia, writing as fast as I can to buffer against inevitable rejection of the last novel manuscript making the rounds with agents who respond favorably to my so-called query letters but then either fail to respond to the manuscripts I send or wait two to seven months before sending kind emails informing me that, although they recognize my talent and admire many aspects of my work, they're *not the best fit* to represent the project.

Working on something new distracts from time that passes without hearing from agents, knowing it's mid-June when the publishing industry takes off for the beach. I picture all the agents with manuscripts on laps, bare feet in sand, and then a strong wind sends pages flying into the ocean, so the agents reach for another manuscript, the pages of which are scattered again by strong wind, so the agents reach for someone else's manuscript and instead of bothering to read the first few pages the agents throw them into the air until the shore break is mucked with more manuscript pages than seaweed.

I'm sure the agents are well-meaning people looking for the best possible work but even if I look on the brightest possible side and give them the benefit of the doubt and try to be as kind and as generous as I can it's impossible not to freak out about the time it takes to respond, and still it's always the same damn form rejection or a somewhat customized form rejection, the same damn recognition of talent and wishes for a successful career followed by the same quick critique or acknowledgment of difficulties in today's economic climate followed by a crushing word of encouragement.

I'm lucky to battle it out on these fronts and engage in psychic warfare with unresponsive agents who receive hundreds of manuscripts a day from committed talented writers who might have more saleable identities, more interesting biographies, and simpler syntax, writers whose sentences don't go on and on, who aerate their manuscripts with innumerable chapter breaks, who insert clever typographical elements or images or PowerPoint slides into the damn text, who experiment with form, who have respected teachers from their MFA programs vouching for them, who have MFA programs listed in their bios, who have excellent publication histories, who have interesting surnames.

Something must be terribly wrong with my writing if someone named Throop Roebling can't get published. Or maybe a name like *Throop Roebling* creates an expectation for something more outrageous, ambitious, experimental, unconventional. Writers' styles so often seem to derive from their names. Carver's carefully carved slices of life. But who cares about names? A name by any other name. It's also possible that agents don't wish to associate themselves with such a name. But the name is a cipher that fills with associations related to the writer's writing. Now when you search my name you see citations for pieces I posted on that weird little lit site, as well as a post on a blog surmising that an editor friend had actually written everything attributed to "Throop Roebling," as though my name were one of his pseudonyms, as though he had written everything posted under my name back in the site's early days when we were inseparable buds, having both moved to Brooklyn around the same time and almost immediately found each other.

I had moved to Brooklyn to live a so-called literary life. I lived with roommates of course but when not working on freelance editing and rudimentary web design I spent every waking hour exaggerating an advanced case of bookish monkishness. I look back on that time as the happiest of my life, the last year of the last century and the first year of the current one. I was focused and disciplined and in good shape since I rarely drank. I was *en fuego*, pure light, or so

I thought, or so I remember having felt. Everything was ahead, everything in the future. There was little sense of the past. If youngish and casually ambitious at the time, it wasn't the worst place to be. I thought it was the best possible place to be, in fact, at first.

Jonathan David Grooms was there too, in a different part of town, where the real writers were, or so we thought. Writers who lived over there seemed older, professional. They worked at *Esquire* and *Details*, *The New Yorker* and *Harper's*. On stage at readings they wore button-downs tucked into dress pants as they read short semi-comedic pieces no one laughed at and then looked down from the stage as though disappointed in the crowd for not laughing at their short semi-comedic pieces that weren't funny.

You could almost see them thinking that Eggers had become this huge literary star and had worked at *Esquire* and they knew what it took to become a huge literary star or at least transform their talent for writing short semi-comedic pieces into six-figure advances for semi-comedic novels or semi-comedic essay collections. Wearing a suit to a reading instead of jeans signaled they were ready for six-figure advances. They deserved at least one six-figure advance, which were relatively common at the time. They seemed to file their literary activities in the Career folder instead of the Art folder and primarily considered how things would help or hurt their career rather than help or hurt their art. They smirked at the crowd not laughing at their short semi-comedic pieces and I remember thinking their dream died right there. Six-figure advance went *poof*. That condescending smirk was saying *c'mon play the game*, y'know the one where I stand up here and you pretend to adore me so I can get paid.

Not five feet from me in these unappreciative crowds, Jonathan David Grooms may have also registered that condescending smirk. But if Grooms were around we never saw him unless he was reading on stage himself. He had done the same thing I had done, at a younger age, to full effect, effortlessly, whereas I'd done it to no effect, with extreme effort. Grooms wrote stories and novels and essays without trying, as far as we knew. He sat in a dark room in front of a computer for a few hours and emerged with a complete short story ready for *The New Yorker* or *Harper's* or *The Paris Review*, one of those three, which took it immediately.

Meanwhile, I handwrote stories and novels and spent hours typing them up, hours I could have been reading or writing or doing anything else, thinking that handwriting was necessary because it freed me from losing the momentum of the story since I constantly polished sentences whenever I wrote on the computer. Handwriting liberated me from perfecting something still in the process of becoming something. Otherwise, it was like working to get the mailbox right, spending so much time on it, and then realizing that the house itself was in a state of shambling incompletion. But handwriting let me write the story without interference. Arm and pen, paper and imagination, synchronized and the world disappeared, only aware of what I imagined, tracing it in jagged ink like a seismograph machine, not sure if I'd ever be able to decipher what I'd written, like it would be lost forever thanks to sloppy penmanship. So there would be time spent composing and then time sitting with laptop and open notebook trying to decipher and type what I'd written. As long as later that day I typed what I'd written, the words, which looked like a child's rendition of seagulls in flight over ocean waves, would return to me in context. An excruciating process that took hours from otherwise enjoying life.

Whole days I devoted to typing my handwritten scrawl, these stories and essays I'd then edit on micro sentence levels and macro structural levels, temporal levels, moving sections around. Once things seemed in order, I'd go to work on the language, making several passes across the rush of words, each sentence a puzzle solved for accuracy, for sensory activation, for economy, for profluence (forward flow) until I couldn't see ways to improve the sentence, and then I'd move to the next and the next and the next.

My greatest fear involved Disembodied Proper Noun Syndrome, that is, uncharacterized character names interacting in a setting that's undescribed so its dimensions can't be sensed. So I focused on characterization and description, and yet when you read Grooms, he rarely describes. Somehow, like Kundera, he overcame Disembodied Proper Noun Syndrome and even made it seem like a trademark. Not filling pages with description gave him more room for action, the characters came alive as they walked and talked and came into conflict with other characters, suggesting conflict within themselves. Grooms ramped up the momentum of the story by giving his characters something they wanted that ran contrary to what other characters wanted. Once the engine of mutually conflicting desires was up and running, his novels combusted on the page and propelled expository jags where he exercised epigrammatic talents and dished wisdom to readers, so his books, despite consisting of Disembodied Proper Nouns walking around undescribed cities and driving around undescribed suburbs, seemed to squirm with characters existing in settings readers were obliged to provide from scratch.

It's assumed Carver didn't describe his characters but descriptions of characters in "Cathedral" are as long and exacting and particular as the description of Timofey at the beginning of Nabokov's *Pnin*. No one would intuitively state that the word count related to initial formative character description in "Cathedral" and *Pnin* favored Carver over Nabokov, like an inverted universe where Nabokov were less of a maximalist than Carver. Compared to Carver and Nabokov, however, Grooms's character description word count in his most recent novel is ridiculously low. Unambiguously gendered names signal male or female but the rest is suggested in the action, emerges in moments of conflict, so there's a halo resting atop the characters' heads whenever Grooms drops some wisdom or humor or anything that expands the scenario from the particular to the universal, the sort of perfectly phrased, meaningful sentences that are underlined, the pages they appear on are dog-eared, phrases recited hundreds of years later. What a piece of work. She should have died hereafter. Whether 'tis nobler in the mind.

I haven't memorized Grooms's best lines but it's like he hurls the reader through the air on the upward curve of a parabola as the story takes off and then when he hits you with a wisdom zinger the bottom drops out and your head spins as the writing soars. Some call that feeling *vertiginous*, sudden awareness of where you are in the world and that although you're seated and reading or, in my case often walking, the world falls away and you're aware you're sitting and reading upon the surface of a planet orbiting a star orbiting something larger orbiting something larger orbiting something so large we can't even conceive of the next unit to name whatever the universe orbits. Whatever that namelessness is, maybe "God," must exist in a system of gods, all spinning through space, orbiting something beyond that, and while inconceivable orbiting enormities exist at light-speed forever in all directions, we're here reading, breathing, concerned with characters whose primary characterizing units are their names and actions and desires, and now we're pulled into that fictional orbit, the rotation of the characters and themes, their rise and fall and reiteration.

The magic trick on Grooms's part is not that we're aware of all this but that we care about the fictional universe he puts in orbit inside us. We care about it in part because it corresponds to our own orbit, our non-fictional subjective universe, so by reading his books or any good books we escape *into* reality, not from it. We escape *into* fictional reality that informs non-fictional reality, ideally, that like a benign psychoactive drug enhances perception of the world around us.

Nabokov says, more or less, the primary objective of fiction is to demonstrate reality's *potentiality* for fiction, or in other words to enhance readers' perception of the world so they see the world as worthy of being written about, so they see lives as potential texts, so they associate disparate qualities of existence and their relation to the so-called great books, so readers at least understand their lives as having something in common with something in the so-called great books, none of which I bet were written by following writing advice parroted by writing teachers parroted by writing students who repeat the decree that *a story teaches the reader how to read it* or *endings should be surprising yet inevitable* and all heads nod in recognition of the wisdom related to the limited freedom of story construction.

I never wanted much to do with the creative writing industry churning out more students with masters of fine arts degrees than there could ever be publications in top literary magazines or published novels by decent major and small presses, the creative writing industry with its annual conference in Chicago or Denver or New York or Boston or Seattle, the whole master of fine arts in creative writing industry an attempt to saturate the marketplace with bloodless anonymous prose, well-crafted luminosity, well-crafted strategic inducements of heartbreak, with writing so well-crafted it's undermined by its craft because its craft is so apparent, craftiness serving a display of craftiness instead of the story the craft is intended to convey across the choppy waters of reading, across the treacherous strait between beginning and end of story, the slip of time between start and finish of story during which the reader is liable to drown in the waters of apathy, of impatience, of cynicism, of eye roll, of dry-eyed death stare at the craftiness of the writing, when what is needed in most cases is a reason for the story to exist other than a deadline for workshop or a literary journal's annual contest, a reason for existence beyond an exercise in point of view that might be worked up and extended and submitted to a dozen literary magazines and emailed to fiction@newyorker.org because their site lists an email for fiction submissions so *why not?* If anything is clear about programs that award a master of fine arts in creative writing, acceptance is a crapshoot, reactions from students are a crapshoot, responses from professors are a crapshoot, the whole thing because a writer's *audacity, authority, execution, oomph,* and *heft* cannot yet be quantified is therefore a total crapshoot.

III.

Most of the year is a struggle to regain the expansiveness of mid-June days, the sense that life is limitless or at least as long as the longest days, sun irradiates and a dazed benevolence comes on, work eases, bosses take vacations, their bosses take vacations, and their bosses take vacations twice as long as those of the hardest-working workers in the world. Spring may be the beginning of the growing season but it's prenatal, cutting back and forth between hot and cold, but once summer heat rolls in and every day is in the eighties and nineties, life begins, limbs loosen, skin on display seems commonplace, and one of the first days clear of fluctuation for the rest of summer is June 16, the day Joyce chose for Bloomsday because his future wife Nora had masturbated him to completion on a Dublin park bench that day, inducing in Joyce a number fixation.

June is the sixth month of the year plus the sixteenth day equals twenty-two. Stephen Dedalus is twenty-two years old, there are twenty-two lines per page in the first edition, twenty-two words in the first sentence of *Ulysses*.

I'm not twenty-two anymore, thank god. I hadn't yet really started writing fiction when I was twenty-two, at most wrote letters, a few poems. The world was filled with tangible, physical correspondence back then. If I'd had a pregnant wife when I was twenty-two, the kid would be driving around, getting ready for college, but maybe since I haven't yet had a child I've remained something of a child myself. Every day and night attending to a child, it must change who you are, how you spend your time, and therefore how you make your living.

Writing and reading are how I make my living, whereas *working* is my job, editorial employment that provides stability and security and health benefits and adequate pay in exchange for not so taxing, relatively interesting labor, although it's been less interesting recently, and more taxing as a result of decreased interest. I'd been thinking about making a change, even if it were a parallel change, but then it became clear we'd need health insurance once my wife was laid off around the time she got pregnant. We would need health insurance for the pregnancy and birth. We had enough savings not to worry for a year but instead of searching for another job I decided I needed to stay at my job and do the best I could during the day to endure it. Before she gave birth I would get as much possible work done on a new novel before we introduced into our lives an offspring that might require some time, energy, and attention. If the timing had been different or the first round of conceptual intercourse hadn't succeeded she would have resumed birth control once we found out she'd been laid off. Instead we will soon have a living human baby person at home, which may require more than simply making my living early in the morning before going to work, working on novels, thinking I take to the consistent hours it requires, how it organizes life, regulates energetic time I have outside of work and forces me to proceed in a healthy manner. Writing novels lets me live this way regardless of publication. In fact, writing novels that are not published makes it clear I do it for the positive regimentation of the hours I have left alive, not for money or praise or prestige or anything other than the work itself.

My two favorite mottos are 1) *work is its own reward* and 2) *"work is its own reward" is the motto of the loser.* I believe in the former more than the latter. The work itself is pure, engagement with text, application of time and talent to the cultivation of the imagination. It's worth it to me and I'll never stop no matter how often I'm asked questions like "are you still writing?" I'll never stop even once they stop asking me questions about it, stop identifying me as a writer, as though failure to publish manuscripts on my hard drive ready for entanglement en masse with the imaginations of readers wipes that part of my identity.

But what if work isn't its own reward? What if *life* is its own reward, and by living half-speed, cruising while talking about anything other than books or writing, I'm not really living life? My writing work, my so-called *reward*, would be more satisfying for myself and others if I were more engaged in anything other than reading and writing, and yet most of my friends are writers who read a good deal, some more than others, but even *they* have begun to fail to ask what I've been working on, what I've been reading, or maybe because I so consistently ask what they've been reading and writing they consider such questions my domain? I'm expected to interview them, essentially, as though I care what they've been reading and writing, which seems true: I want to live a life in which friends read and write and talk about writing and reading in such a way that doesn't make me want to puke.

The difficulty with having friends who talk about writing and reading is that such talk might make me distrust the instinct animating their reading and writing. Grilling writer friends so they don't feel like they're being grilled controls the conversation, moves them in the direction I'd like to go, talking about editing or character construction or reading or, more often than not these days, trying to get agents.

We've all finished novel manuscripts we send to agents hoping they'll represent these novel manuscripts and coax editors into buying them and converting them into published books that make top ten lists at the end of the year and win an award or at least are shortlisted. The one of us who has an agent has been asked to submit a major revision of his novel. It never stops for anyone, jumping through hoops. But most of us are still trying to finish novels worthy of representation by an agent or acceptance by a small press editor.

Writers all over the world are trying to sell their manuscripts and get deals that involve future unwritten novels, securing time and prestige where they teach, which may in turn lead to the long-term security of tenure (the word reminds me of *pasture*).

Writers all over the world are trying to achieve commercial success to accompany critical success or critical success to match commercial success.

Writers all over the world want their commercially and critically successful novels turned into movies or series starring famous actors who will appear on the cover of cheap airport-edition paperbacks.

Writers all over the world want to win the National Book Award, the Pulitzer Prize, the Booker Prize, the National Book Critics Award, the PEN/Faulkner or another PEN award, and they want their books released by Vintage Classics or Modern Library and ideally win a MacArthur "genius" grant, a Guggenheim, a National Endowment for the Arts grant, and be in line for a Nobel once their career comes into view and is seen as something of a miracle.

All over the world, writers are trying to figure out how to feed one sentence into the one that follows it, to write well enough that an editor at a semi-respectable online literary journal or academic literary journal might consider it and then offer to post it online or publish it in print.

We've all passed that first step. We're all confident that, in general, we are publishable. We can write well enough and at times I'm sure each one of us thinks we will one day achieve a sliver of a semblance of the critical and commercial success of someone like Jonathan David Grooms. That day will only come if we work as well as we can, if we stick to routine, hone our craft, sharpen the blades of our art, and put ourselves in a position to succeed.

Flannery O'Connor said you have to put yourself in a chair on the beach so you're present when lightning strikes: it's about habit, the writing habit, like a serious drug habit except much cheaper, other than opportunity costs (the cost of all things not done when writing, including working on freelance jobs or generally enjoying life).

Laws about readying yourself for the lightning strike did not seem to apply to Jonathan David Grooms, however, who can't seem to express a stray thought without someone publishing it, without seeing it printed in an article or essay, without it being posted immediately from someone's phone and analyzed for insight into his work and character.

Far in the future, our descendants will encounter pronouncements, observations, descriptions, and scenes enacted by characters Jonathan David Grooms brought into the world. We always say that if Grooms hadn't existed we would have needed to invent him to fill the void after so many writers who'd made their names in the twentieth century transitioned to the spirit world. Some reading and writing practitioners and enthusiasts perceived a crisis atop the American writing pyramid even if writers cannot be ranked since there's no equivalent to slugging percentage or home run tally.

The rage to order and rank, to quantify the unquantifiable: at one point the goal had been to utter the unutterable, go out into desert and sit atop twenty-foot tower and chant until the resonance in your chest blew your mind. Now it's about quantifying what cannot be counted, assigning numerical significance to abstract attributes, like authority, audacity, execution, oomph, heft. The old verities listed by Faulkner in his Nobel Prize speech, how might they be quantified? A writer scores highly in compassion but not in courage. Characters seem to live thanks to precise spare description. There's plentiful dialogue and readers can see more of the world than the characters can, so it's suspenseful as we wait for characters to turn a corner in their lives and either meet the occasion or more often than not crumple under the pressure of a moment they hadn't seen coming in which their dreams are crushed.

The hopes of characters are so often dashed because the hopes of writers are so often dashed upon the rocks of rejection or bad reviews or total lack of attention and response, let alone commercial success. Writers like to say the whole thing's a crapshoot (that's the word used, *crapshoot*) and so of course more often than not the house wins whenever writers lose, and the writers, with hopes for the smallest possible success, smash against the rocks of the worst that can happen to their dream of the least bit of reward for maximum effort expended.

A hundred-thousand words become set in their sentences like lyrics of a song, every phrase tested for economy and sensory-activation and rhythmic flowing buoyancy, like a bed so well-made the reader's eye bounces like a dime off the tension of the forward-flowing propulsion of language, a ticket to a glittering city that will open once the carefully composed, smart, funny, moving novel is presented to the world like a letter of introduction, payoff for all those hours alone, the Big Change always hoped for and worked toward received in exchange for all the effort: accolades, financial reward, an all-encompassing embrace from the culture.

Characters so rarely see dreams realized because writers so rarely achieve anything approaching reward for their so-called *work*. Characters' hopes are so consistently crushed because writers' hopes are so consistently crushed. The word *writer* derives from a word in an ancient language that means someone who started out idealistic and ended embittered but despite crushing defeat after crushing defeat nevertheless endures to embody the cliché about doing the same thing over and over again and expecting different results.

One day the writer will write something worthwhile, if the writer keeps working the writer may even be struck by lightning: organize the clattering jagged shards of life into something that coheres and harmonizes and rounds off in a way that demonstrates the ability of art to achieve transcendence when it engages the actualities of existence instead of simply nodding at them.

All this applies more to me than it does to friends gathering to celebrate the one hundred and eighth anniversary of Bloomsday and the appearance of Jonathan David Grooms once he finishes reading the Molly Bloom soliloquy at the end of the all-day reading event at the Rosenbach Museum, the keynote address of sorts, the incantation of *yeses* at the end of *Ulysses*.

Yes, I say yes, yes, Molly says at the end, an affirmation of everything.

Grooms will come once he's finished reading, once he signs copies of books and the little program they create with the roster of readers, none of them ever any of us who commune each year and undergo exploratory group talk therapy and reenact the old-fashioned story arc, the forty-five degree ascent to a climax before we stumble home and next morning are broken all the way down before we return to our senses in time, regain capabilities, and in some ways emerge renewed, refreshed, and ready to recommit to the effort.

IV.

I've never really worried about how much I drink but with wife on couch producing child I know I'll have to limit it in the future. I never slur, I'm never a loud or violent drunk, although I've been argumentative more than once, in part because drink speeds tongue and coordinates thoughts, like touch typing two-hundred words a minute, as close as possible to perfect fluency, without self-consciousness or slip-up or saying anything I'll later regret, releasing what I'd thought but hadn't said or said with a sleepy post-work tongue, all too sober, to wife over dinner, rough draft attempts at articulation like sensing a reservoir of material below the surface, standing there and then lying flat across the earth, sensing the presence of something down there, something serious worth excavating, and then digging with fingers or a stick or trowel, creating starting points for further work and future exploration, and over time while working or walking or exercising or showering the entryways are widened and deepened in silence. Consumption of a third pint of India Pale Ale is like an oil digger that sends you straight into earth tenderized where you've worked it, an underground reservoir of thought becomes accessible and you convey to the surface the contents of subterranean caverns with each glass until what's retrieved sounds the same as what came up at first. Each glass retrieves less material, caverns close up, you can't access it anymore, and the next day you sense a fissure across the surface of your skull, something you know will heal in a day or so. Something was gained, something not so well understood was stated with fluency, the person you talked with got something out of it and gave something in return and it all made sense and seemed like it jus-tified the price of the pints and rough morning. Excavation work was worth it, not to mention the story arc, rising exhilaration and climax and denouement and the little lift of recovering the next day having had an experience, having entered a tunnel reverberating with asso-ciations from which you emerge maybe somewhat changed.

A good story or novel works that way too, the story like an expe-rience through which a reader emerges maybe somewhat changed. But that sounds like creative writing talk, the sort of thing that no matter how good it sounds, no matter how much sense it makes, nevertheless makes me want to rebel, contradict it, mock it, if only because it's a parroted articulation, as though repeating something about a *reverberating chamber of associations* has merit when repeated and repeated and repeated.

All in all because I don't want to associate myself with it I unfurl sheets of language down the page, an act with its own anti-craft craft-work, its own unconventional anti-structure. It's the way I want to write, knowing that doing so hurts chances of publishing, especially longer pieces. If I want to publish novels with a major publishing company or a well-regarded independent press, I should not sub-mit blocks of language that refuse to include a few hundred hard re-turns.

I left New York for a city ninety miles to the southwest where my rent dropped from $700 for a shared apartment to under $300 for a room in a dilapidated Victorian near the Penn campus before I met my wife and moved to a rowhome we bought in South Philly, where I've since articulated arguments against the hard return, against pressing the ← enter button on my keyboard at opportune moments to inform the reader they should pay attention to the phrase preced-ing the hard return.

I would try not to learn another thing about writing that could be taught and instead learn in such a way that seems formless at first but that involves numerous restrictions, like parenthood, like anything really, and so I decided the sprawling density of a block of language would make my name, Throop Roebling.

I would associate myself with the one-paragraph novel and those who practiced the one-paragraph novel: Thomas Bernhard and Bohumil Hrabal and not too many others, Stephen Dixon, Horacio Castellanos Moya, László Krasznahorkai, Andreas Maier, Mathias Énard. The one-paragraph novel is identified as "Bernhardian" because Bernhard seems to have created the form and perfected it, an ideal conveyor of theme and variation, an ideal vehicle for energetic prose and humor, the language always pushing ahead and turning back on itself, sentences pushing ahead before they turn back on themselves.

I decided to write in a modified Bernhardian mode, not imitate Bernhard exactly, not rant about Austria and suicide and how Austrians are only good at suicide, of everything Austrians do well it is suicide they do best, if they're geniuses at anything they're geniuses at suicide. Instead of writing about Austrian suicide I'd use the form to write about life in a way that felt urgent and energetic and actual instead of fictional. The form washed through it and made it all seem more real than conventionally formatted prose that always felt false to me, fake, parroted, restricted to the point of genre, no different than horror or erotica or thriller or crime genres. The literary fiction genre follows just as many restrictions and little laws, including blending other genres and inclusion of sections toward the end that seem to break out of the narrative progression and yet nevertheless feel inevitable. "Surprising yet inevitable" is the most parroted phrase when it comes to endings in the conventional literary fiction genre, and anyone who cares more about reading than they do about writing, who cares about creating something entertaining and edifying for readers, ideally, should be concerned about conventional literary form and its deathtraps, its sinkholes, its ability to transform the terrific into the terrible with a twist of syntax or overextended simile.

I don't want to have anything to do with it except it's all I have beyond wife and job and family and imminent child, having decided some years earlier that I would no longer follow sports. I calculated that I wasted way too many hours half-watching televised sporting events as I half-read articles and half-thought about what I was writing, what I'd written, what I intended to write, all while not writing anything. If I wanted to achieve through the loose unregulated framework of writing the literary equivalent of walk-off home runs I would need to commit to the writing effort. I didn't need to spend time half-watching an athletic event as I half-read something on my phone. Instead I focused on achieving the ideal of my writing effort.

Cutting out so much noise flooded me with time for writing and reading, and I effortlessly produced the best novel I've written, the most accessible, the funniest, the saddest, the truest. I sent it to the agents whose rejections of previous efforts had been kind and encouraging, and those agents again agreed to look at my writing, thinking this time I will slip through cracks and somehow manage to publish something that's not conventional crap. It's not necessarily probable but it's certainly possible, conceivable, feasible. Grooms has done it, of course, repeatedly. He camps out on the sweet spot between convention and experimentation and produces books that read more like enjoyable smart funny sad literature than literary fiction, that simply by creating engaging voices it seems like he can do anything, like David Foster Wallace without overt pathologies and relentless ironic recursivity, and not as self-conscious about seduction of readers with pyrotechnics and humor and compassion and footnotes. Grooms is more understated, more accessible to what remains of the once-great masses of readers now huddled drinking wine in book clubs. His writing is open and aerated with easy lofted confident prose that feels at its default level like an extraordinary basketball player gliding back on defense after driving the lane and dunking in traffic. Really it's only been Grooms who's been able to transcend concerns regarding the state of the so-called *Lit World*.

Grooms entered the so-called *Lit World* fully formed and used its good and its noxious citizens to promote and disperse his manuscripts to readers, the way every writer would ideally be published, with agents, editors, critics, booksellers, everyone united charging into the mêlée equipped with the latest cultural weaponry in the form of a new novel by Jonathan David Grooms. When he has a new manuscript he sends it to his agent and the agent reads it right away and the only question that occurs to the agent when presented with *the event* of a new manuscript by Jonathan David Grooms is how much will it sell for, how much more can he get for it than he got for the last novel, and should they consider giving a break to the publisher as long as the publisher agrees to also publish novels they otherwise wouldn't publish?

Lao Guardian once informed everyone that Grooms takes a lower initial advance if the publisher agrees to publish literary titles each year they ordinarily wouldn't take a chance on. These so-called *Grooms Books* are selected and blurbed by him and talked up in interviews whenever possible, and so there's added impetus to go out tonight even if doing so suggests we're not just there for Bloomsday.

Instead of celebrating the true beginning of the year, our friendship, another successful year of life, and the idea of the masterpiece more than the masterpiece itself, we'll gather for Grooms's sake, to see if we can list ourselves among the writers working for money when writing. Unless paid an advance, writers who say they've been *working* should say they've been working for no pay. If writing is your primary income, you're working, sure, but you can't say you're working if what you work on won't be paid for. Pay for writing is welcomed, of course, but once an hourly rate is calculated it's well below minimum wage, and that doesn't include start-up costs, all those years of unpaid effort, writing, reading, living, whatever else is re-quired to create something someone might be willing to pay for.

If I go out tonight I'll be living in the future, and since I have hope for the publication of work that hasn't yet occurred I know if I at-tend Bloomsday all my hopes will be dashed. I'll be self-conscious and argumentative. Instead of sucking up to Grooms I'll openly crit-icize him. I'll undercut his novels to his face. Say he's only successful because his approach is so moderate and the secret to his success is how well he straddles the fence between conventionality and exper-imentation. I'll call him a fence-straddling centrist with short-term charisma but there's no way his books will stand over time. Instead of engaging in all that crap, I'll stay home and write and get to bed early with super-pregnant wife and wake up early on Sunday June 17 and push my embryonic novel manuscript toward viability.

Every word is a cell that replicates. Cellular replication com-pounds until the manuscript comes alive. *Coming alive* means the sur-face of the manuscript disappears as it reveals the world of the story, characters, setting, themes, all of it existing only in the imagination of a writer at first and also ultimately in the imaginations of readers if things go well. But before imaginations can intertwine there must be boatloads of work, hours spent doing something for no pay, hours spent not doing everything human beings might do other than sit alone and work for no pay, for example go out and confront Grooms, do something that at least for our handful of writer reader drinker friends becomes *news that stays news*, as Ezra Pound said about litera-ture.

I have to go out and create literature itself, something written about in the future, a novel in itself. I will be there not as another Bloomsday attendee but as a character talked into being by an unreli-able narrator, an older European man, an older *dead* European man, someone not quite sober or sane when alive or read much these days except by a handful of writers like me.

I will turn the night into art, something we write about, a collaborative version of *Rashomon* or *The Sound and Fury* in a style like that of a late Joseph Roth novel.

It's the least I can do for Bloomsday, give us a night to write about, a night that enters the canon of great nights, a night that will be read about and considered fictional thanks to so many varying accounts of what happened.

Knowing I will suffer because I'm thinking too much about the future I decide to go out and create that suffering in advance, anticipate it, bring it into the world and own it, take responsibility for what I do and what I write and for the child inside my wife asleep on the couch wearing stretchy black Capri-style pants, not stirring as I down a glass of red wine and then another before I slip out of the house and make my way through empty streets toward the bar.

V.

There's still some light left in the sky, what's left of the most beautiful day, a day spent loading books on new floor-to-ceiling shelves and then walking while reading one of those books. Re-establishing the bookshelf signaled a new start to the year, a new beginning, a flag planted in the procession of time. Not only was it the one hundred and eighth anniversary of the day *Ulysses* takes place on June 16, 1904, but also the day we moved all books from floor and tabletop to newly erected bookshelf, shelves stained mahogany and secured to the wall, fastened in such a way that a toddler might not pull a vertical beam and bring the whole thing down on his head.

I say *his head* because I anticipate a boy. I see a son pulling down our temple of books, although we don't know if the in utero infant is a boy or girl at this point. I can see him when I'm doing dishes come into the kitchen at age seven or so, thick hair a little long with bangs cut just above the eyebrows. I can see him like a ghost entering the room, a future physical presence in our corner of the world loaded now with shelves and books, weighed down the way it feels to have packed some muscle on your arms and shoulders, heavier on the scale but stronger, able to lift whatever. The shelves feel like that. Buying the shelves and staining them, setting them up, and then spending hours arranging books in *associative order* strengthens our tall narrow rowhome, solidifies what will come, taking shape in my wife, solidifying into natal form, rounding out what had once been her solid core.

Instead of writing on Saturday morning, we finished securing the shelves to the wall we'd painted a charcoal black upon which the mahogany shelves loaded with colorful spines seem to hover as the wall recedes or at least makes the boundaries of the room behind the bookshelf seem ambiguous, and then began the hours of entertainment known as arranging books on shelves in associative instead of alphabetical order.

The bookshelf had been smaller and on the opposite wall but we moved it across the room and expanded it so the kitchen table would be where the shelf had been, creating more flow through the long narrow rowhome from living-room windows in front through the dining room library area through the kitchen through the little mud room through the back door to the cement patio out back with its approximation of an urban garden paradise. Moving the bookshelves creates a flow of light from eastern front to western back and back to front, not only an unimpeded flow of light but also an obstacle-less track for the cats to run back and forth chasing each other, treating one another as prey, and with the books along the northern wall of the dining room library area and the table across the narrow room against the southern wall and out of the flow from western back to eastern front and vice versa everything seemed after more than a year living in this newly renovated rowhome caught in a cross-streaming current of light and cats and vision thanks to this little change my wife insisted on and I resisted at first because I didn't want to move the shelves when she'd wanted to move them because she was pregnant and I was stressed at work, I realized, also stressed about everything related to writing work, stressed by silence on the part of agents not responding about my most recent novel manuscript, stressed by wife losing her job, no way of knowing if we'd make our reasonable mortgage payments or have to sell and move, and so everything we'd established over the past year in the new house, the garden out back, all the little decisions about the arrangement of couches and desks and dressers and lamps, all of it was endangered, I felt, even more so in the fall after we conceived what most likely will turn out to be a healthy human child emerging in early July, a child without wings or flippers or horns and tail and cloven feet, we hope, a child more or less healthy and ready to take on the world once his parents are beaten down by chronic exposure to life over time and he's ready to inherit the bookshelf as long as he promises not to impose meaningless *alphabetical order* on the bookshelves his father spent hours arranging so Handke flows into Musil into Bernhard into Schulz into Kis into Gracq into Joseph Roth into Kafka into Faulkner into DeLillo into David Foster Wallace into Houellebecq into Bret Easton Ellis into Philip Roth into Auster into Leyner into Saunders into Gogol into Tolstoy into Proust, all these little clumps of the writing of white male writers, and the boy, one quarter something other than white, will look upon these spines and see something of his father there, an abstract self-portrait in thick, slender, and in-between multi-colored spines, each of which on the inside at first uniformly consists of black words on white pages except the pages are really more gray or cream-colored or the color of the skin of an ancient jaundiced librarian as still and slow to move as his books, the text in varied shapes and sizes, all the fonts, the margins never uniform, the language rarely anonymous, the ideas distinct, the approaches unpredictable, all of it accessible should the son ever sit in silence and hold a book in front of him and see into worlds he might never guess were there at first if he had only noticed the gold-and-black spines of the Musil, the Mann, the Roth, the Faulkner, the thickest DeLillo.

The Throop Roebling Memorial Bookshelf of Undeniable Excellence my son will inherit, the shelves will bridge the space between the years it took to gather these spines and read what's in them and associate them with worlds within other books and then arrange and rearrange them on mahogany-stained shelves, arranged as though they're important in the world, in my world at least, something without which I can't imagine my son seeing into the past, seeing into the worlds I've seen into, sharing these experiences, the texts letting him in on these secret spots accessible for free, if he's patient and silent and lets their language activate his imagination.

The best ever, the very best, the peak, the top of the peak, the bits above the peak hovering in air, hanging above the peak like volcano smoke or needy ragged strip of gauzy cloud, it's something I've needed in my life, so it's something I want in our child's life, something we'll have available when needed to stand against everything I imagine he'll encounter and everything I can't possibly foresee, the technological challenges of the second quarter of the twenty-first century, the economic and environmental and emotional shitstorms he'll navigate. At all times he'll have this failsafe compass in the form of a wall of books associatively arranged while he was in utero by his father, this writer reader who walks and reads and then sits alone and writes about walking and reading.

What a strange father for someone to have in the early twenty-first century, unlike dads we see when we take ill-advised trips to one of the enormous malls to the northeast or northwest or southeast of the city. Other dads don't seem concerned with such matters and certainly do not seem to champion and defend and raise their sons to champion and defend such concerns as though they're an endangered persecuted religious sect, *Literary Fundamentalists* engaged in shadowy battle for the soul of the country's citizens against well-established forces that don't try to quell the insurgency because they don't know such an insurgency exists. It's meaningless to them, so mysterious it might as well not exist, this wall of books, this walker reader who writes about walking and reading and thinks at times he's doing something nobler than walking miles and reading pages. The chip on the shoulder of the walking reader the size of a monument in the shape of *War and Peace*, any of those immortal masterpieces, like *Ulysses*, which on this day we celebrate because it's Bloomsday, June 16, the one hundred and eighth anniversary of the day *Ulysses* takes place.

More than a hundred years later nothing is different, only a handful of those who've been natured and nurtured to appreciate such things care about such things whereas for the most part no one even knows such books exist or at most if they know June 16 is Bloomsday they think it's a quaint, quirky, bookish, nerdy/cool thing to celebrate, as good as any other excuse to celebrate, sure, even if most everyone celebrates holidays based on much older masterpieces, and so maybe we're all apostles of what will one day, long after the Literary Fundamentalist takeover of the United States of America, become a new national holiday.

Bloomsday will be the *new* New Year's, the new official start of the year. Instead of an enormous disco ball descending in Times Square it will be a projection of stately plump Buck Mulligan descending the stairs with his shaving razor and mirror, the new start for the culture once the first official meeting of the American Literary Fundamentalist Movement convenes.

With cores of soul and home solidified with associatively arranged bookshelves my unborn son will inherit and use to protect himself against the inadequacies of the world, I need to convince Grooms and friends that the time is right for a *Literary Fundamentalist* takeover of the United States of America. Nothing less is called for, nothing less can we hope for, nothing less than inciting this takeover is appropriate at this moment in our lives. We have a moral obligation to lead a revolution of walking reading literary foot soldiers.

It would be a nonviolent passive-resistance approach to taking over the country, and of course I don't see how we can take over the country, even with Jonathan David Grooms as the face of the movement, even if he leads an endless procession of walking readers right down Broadway, thousands of Literary Fundamentalists taking to the streets, walking while reading literature from the late-nineteenth century or early-twentieth century, at most late-twentieth century masterpieces, mostly European fiction but also stray American titles.

The density of the book in the hand matters since it elevates the degree of difficulty to such an extent that the density of all these novels, all these pages turned over the course of the walking and reading, turns the walking reading procession into a spectacle liable to enter the conventional media bloodstream. The density of the novels and the purported difficulty of the prose compound until the language consumed during *the libambulatory procession* synchronizes with consciousnesses spurred by elevated pulses thanks to a reasonable walking reading pace.

I feel how sore my legs are, walking now to the bar, since after loading books onto shelves in associative order for what felt like hours I took off with *Ulysses* and re-read its last thirty pages, the long single-sentence soliloquy by Molly Bloom. I read as I walked first along one river and then across the city until I reached the other river. I then walked up that river five miles until I came to a bridge and then I walked back to the city on a path along the other side of the river and limped home with thighs chaffed and aflame. I walked as though straddling something unseen, like an old stiff cowboy walking while reading the last pages of *Ulysses*, saturating myself in Molly Bloom's thoughts as Joyce believed they may have appeared to her one hundred and eight years ago. Consciousness isn't a stream of language as much as a mix of still and moving images overdubbed with stray words. Joyce must have known this but presented it as a long sentence instead of something more like a graphic novel or art film or gif.

I walked and read down to the river and up through the city and along the river loop and then back through the city and home. I'm not sure how fast I walked or how many times I read the final chapter but the day was the sort that justifies all human industry, all existence elevated by light breeze, blue sky, feathery clouds, thick shadows, the sun like a child's depiction in yellow and orange marker with exaggerated rays pulsating more like caresses than anything carcinogenic, weather that heals sickness, irradiates body and mind with something almost like affection if not full-on love, the fulfillment of atmospheric lust to pleasure the flesh of all humanity.

I felt healed and almost fulfilled on certain inexplicable subcutaneous semi-sexual solar levels as I walked, all the stress of office work and writing work and home life, super-pregnant wife at home clipping coupons to save a few dollars although we should be good until the baby's first birthday, doing what she can to recognize the necessity of thrift as though minor gestures (saving on black beans and romaine lettuce) will be recognized by a karmic deity who will restore our comfortable dual household income after sufficient time has passed and worry expended.

There's nothing like walking to relieve stress, nothing like reading to upend it, that is, as long as you're not so stressed you can't concentrate on what you're reading, as long as you can imagine what's written on the page, let the words trigger images you see existing somewhere within the text, ahead of you, above you, within you, the text triggering images that intermix with everything you pass while walking and reading, all of it peripheral except for the book held so close-range obstacles are seen well in advance of impact, the book held out like a talisman, a totem, a standard for all to see, an unpaid advertisement for the author, the book, and myself, for this conspicuous display of mind and body healthfulness, the cover visible to all, asserted with pride into the space in front of me like a scythe that cuts right to left with every turned page.

Walking while reading the last chapter of *Ulysses* means that most of the book's weight fell to my left hand, almost the entire novel was swung to its left side whereas only a few pages were on the right, a thin slip of pages, but it didn't feel like an accomplishment to have all the weight on the left and so little on the right because I'd read the book long ago. I'd read it with a guidebook like I was visiting a foreign city. I'd prepared for reading the book like I was preparing for going on vacation. On a Friday afternoon I returned from my job at a bookstore back then and didn't leave my bedroom until Monday morning, awake maybe eighteen hours a day, tearing through *Ulysses*. I can't remember what season it was when I'd read it, the atmosphere in the room like March or April, warm enough but not expansive, unlike this Bloomsday morning when the world seemed wide open, when the pages I turned toward the end of *Ulysses* each seemed like a step toward alleviation of stressors.

I walked too fast and read too fast and even upon re-reading missed too much, since the text seemed studded with sinkholes, Molly's point of view so deep it seemed cellular. All I could do was trace the contours of former impacts upon the surface of her earth. If crossed too quickly these soft moist craters of her past trapped my attention as I walked and read, holding the book in front of me as I walked along the river loop, tall trees and bikers and slow walkers in exercise gear, serious shirtless runners on pace for personal bests, everyone else out for some morning exercise, making an effort. No matter the accelerated pulse thanks to walking fast now for miles with the pages held ahead of me whenever I crossed a sinkhole in the text it sent me into thoughts about the end of what had been a long-standing distracting situation at work, a situation that would end in fact on Monday. Incredible it could go on so long and seem like it would never end without serious intervention and then the end was in sight when the woman who sat next to me for two years gave two weeks' notice.

For two years, maybe more, I'd dreamed of the end of this situation at work, thoughts about my colleague who for two years sat next to me and at most fake-worked while she played games online or managed her social media profiles or e-mailed or shopped or posted on a baby blog. She worked no more than two hours a day at most whereas I worked most of the day, taking breaks now and then of course but mostly I spent the day working as well as I could on what I was paid to work on. It wasn't unreasonable to expect that in exchange for a reasonable salary with excellent benefits and lax dress code and flex time that one would do the job one was hired to do. But instead of working she played games online and managed her social media profiles and posted on baby blogs and shopped more than she worked on what we were paid to work on. After a while it felt like my job to notice this, track her slacking, comprehend the degree to which she wasn't working while at work, and so while walking and reading along the river I read a phrase embedded in Molly's past and seconds later I was back in the office, my slacker colleague slumped over as she played a game that involved clicking little gold icons that fell from the sky.

I once asked her what was the name of the game she played all the time and she said Bejeweled Blitz and I said you must be really good at it. She said she'd played it for years, but she wasn't catching my drift, indirect censure about shirking duties at work to what I'd begun to deem an immoral degree, but then I would put the book down and take in the sights, the trees, the runners, the bikers, the walkers, the rowers in their narrow little boats on the river, the statues along the walkways, some graceful and lithe on pedestals that made them seem to float across the surface of the river, some clunkier as though sculpted by fascists, and I'd forget my slacker colleague and return to the book and immerse myself as I stepped ahead, walking and reading applied to my soul like a dual-action transdermal patch.

It felt like cramming for a test scheduled to begin in eight hours, nine hours, in fewer than ten hours I would no longer be walking and reading the end of *Ulysses* but the great Jonathan David Grooms would be reading aloud while standing in front of a room of people, the great Jonathan David Grooms in town to read the Molly Bloom section aloud as the headliner of the all-day *Ulysses* reading every June 16 at the Rosenbach Museum. In a few hours Jonathan David Grooms will read what I'm reading, I thought as I walked, how will he read these lines, I thought, how would I read them, will I ever be asked to read at the Bloomsday reading event, will I ever be asked to headline it, am I even on the radar as someone to read from *Ulysses*, even from an early chapter, nothing too special, maybe the one in the newsroom with all the wind and fart jokes, metempsychotic analogue to a windy spot along Odysseus's travels? Am I really interested in being recognized as a writer in town worthy of reading from *Ulysses*, am I so desperate for validation, reading aloud from the book to an audience instead of walking and reading it silently and alone, dreaming off about reading it aloud in front of people who specifically asked me to read to them, like to little children I read to them the famous ending of their Bloomsday story, their sweet little stream-of-consciousness story to cap a masterpiece they read once a year, none of them staying and listening to the whole thing, popping in and out, there for the first scene, the ceremonial intonation of "Stately plump," the "S" filling the first page, a description of minor character Buck Mulligan, Stephen's housemate in a tower by the river, descending the stairs but also a description of the novel itself, recognition of a reader's initial reaction to the book. Why yes it sure seems *stately* and it sure is *plump*, among the most famous phrases in the book, the others being "History is a nightmare from which I'm trying to awake," and another being something about *metempsychosis*, about Hamlet and Shakespeare, about Hamlet being Shakespeare's father, about the transmigration of souls, I can't remember exactly. I walked and read along the river during the late morning and early afternoon on Bloomsday, putting myself in caloric deficit in advance of extreme caloric indulgence I anticipated at night. Every mile more or less equaled another beer I could drink, if I decided to go out.

But mostly I walked and read because walking and reading is what I do at this point. It's my thing. I've associated myself with it. The act of walking and reading is a close associate. If something about walking and reading is ever posted online I receive the link from a friend. It's like I somehow converted to some strange new religion, practicing a form of yoga that involves walking and reading but no poses or stretching or concentration on breath, although at times I'm conscious to improve my posture by holding the book a little higher. It's good for shoulders and arms to hold a book at a sixty-degree angle, approximately, not a ninety-degree angle from the ground, which may seem a little aggressive, not a one-hundred-and-twenty degree angle from the ground as though blocking out mid-morning sun, but a sixty-degree angle, ahead of me but still a little down, sometimes conscious that I should ensure that I don't slant too far over the book, that my body itself isn't angled at forty-five degrees but more like eighty. I try at times to tense the muscles of my torso, my chest and stomach and biceps, as I walk. I try to stand straighter, use wind resistance as an obstacle that's easy enough to overcome, and train myself to make an effort more than simply walking and reading for sixteen miles on a beautiful day, which requires no real effort from me.

It's something I do with ease until moisturizer applied to inner thighs wears off and the friction either causes the skin down there to burst into flame or bleed or both. Toward the end of these more than half-marathon libambulation sessions, if fire and blood erupted from my crotch I would not be surprised. It wouldn't surprise me to see flames burst from crotch and consume my shorts while blood flows from between legs and trails behind me in a thick liquid mess. Spontaneous crotch area combustion caused by inner thigh friction would not surprise me but otherwise all areas other than my volatile to the point of potentially flammable inner thigh area are in a state of exceptional relaxation, all the stressors of work, writing work, home life, and life in the world eased to the point of nonexistence.

My mind and body and soul are refreshed to the point of amnesia, as though a sixteen-mile libambulation session on a beautiful mid-June morning are a sip from the river of forgetfulness, in the best possible way, since memory, albeit exquisitely literary, can torture. At some deep level, when otherwise not exhausted, memory associates experiences and scraps of knowledge and novels and films and then, via anxious channels in the brain and body, memory projects worries about the future that the body experiences as stress. The brain sees potential layoff, miscarriage, deformity, rejection, illness, death, bankruptcy, withered garden, clogged toilet, leaky roof, peeling paint, blown light fixture, all the things that can possibly go wrong with a human body, with a household, with finances, with friends, on and on. Shoulders hunch, tension creeps in and settles down for good, and none of it really exists although anticipatory anxiety related to events that may never come lets you ensure they never come by taking arms against them in advance. There's a constant flow of potential stressors even among things that seem to run smoothly, but a sixteen-mile libambulation session washes that sensation from the body, cleans it out, and all those potential stressors persist but are swamped by extreme, exceptional full-body exhaustion.

Somehow despite having walked sixteen miles while reading that morning and afternoon I still am able to walk to the bar where we plan to celebrate Bloomsday after certain preparations including pulling down pants and applying generous portions of creamy moisturizer to hot pink inner thighs, before drinking two quick glasses of wine. My inner thighs looked like a topographical map of Arizona, raised mountain chains of dry sun-roasted terrain, inhospitable to say the least, but generous smears of cooling creamy moisturizer soothe them, coat them in such a way that I am able to make it all the way to the bar, the few blocks to the bar, where I lift my left arm about as high as I held the book earlier in the day to grasp the handle on the bar's door and somehow, despite soreness in left shoulder, I have the strength to pull it open.

VI.

A sudden influx of light startles everyone as the jukebox introduces a tough riff from "Sticky Fingers." I do a Jagger pout and neck juke and turn to the blackboard near the door on which the names of all the beers are written in white chalk next to a sketch of the vessel and price. There are too many choices, too many beers on tap, too many bottles available, too many people at the bar at this hour. It's not yet dark, won't be for a while, yet the windows don't let in much light. Those already here seem like they've spent the day responding to the progressively multiplying possibilities of life by asking the bartender to please pour another pint, although most beers available today come in smaller goblet form.

There's always a local craft beer for four dollars but the others cost more, up to eight dollars, especially those served in goblets with alcohol levels approaching ten percent. Beer becoming more like wine and whisky, expensive and strong, for savoring the aroma, appreciating the anti-gravity effervescence of goat-piss champagne. So many choices but at a place with such an extravagant and apparently often rare selection it seems almost rude to ask for a whisky.

I always look for a pint under six dollars, and I try to choose something from Great Lakes or Southern Tier or other breweries I can count on, opting for pilsners and wheat beers in the summer, India pale ales and porters in the fall, stouts and double IPAs in the winter to get through longer nights. I'm sure semi-sober regulars recognize me from when, before I married, I often spent weekday late-afternoons reading while drinking the half-price happy-hour specials. Reading and drinking, a special pastime, albeit sedentary, to read and order half-off fancy beers served in goblets until the words on the page unsettle, and then pop outside and bum a smoke from someone I've targeted as a friendly generous sort and then return to unfinished beer and unfinished book.

It's all so unfinished. The work ahead is pleasure. If we're to live a semi-decadent, inexpensive American life in a large reviving northeastern city let's enjoy a book and a beer quietly alone instead of anything else we could do that might not seem so considerate. Walking home from drinking and reading I could be jumped by a pack of six-year-old children. But tonight I've left the book at home in order to create literature in the form of life.

I stand on toes to see over everyone standing behind those seated at the bar to see if England and Snare are here. They said they'd come early for food. Staring down the blackboard with the beer list, I presume all fourteen on tap are excellent but two will offer transit to other worlds. Is this the toughest decision I face on a regular basis, deciphering an elaborate beer menu?

I've been here a few hundred times since I moved from Brooklyn less than a hundred miles southwest for more room to live, cheaper rent, an increase in psychological and physical space, a sense that I work for something other than my landlord's prosperity, that if I stayed in I wasn't missing out on everything going on every night, the city's streets flexing in a relentless show of strength, the sidewalks like arms flowing with the blood of life, the people on the streets on perfect nights like cells pulsing vessel to vessel, block to block. To sit home and read was a waste of space, a waste of money, a waste of the blood of life in my veins, so I moved to the closest affordable city with a Chinatown, a subway, and four major sports teams. But mainly I moved because it was comparatively inexpensive.

I didn't feel like I'd lost as much as I'd gained in Philadelphia, no longer feeling that pull when the windows were open, to wander without a book, ten, fifteen miles, up and around and across and back downtown and then over the Brooklyn Bridge and all over and back through Hasidic neighborhoods, West Indian neighborhoods, Boricua neighborhoods, Dominican neighborhoods, hipster neighborhoods, until I returned to the Polish neighborhood I'd called home.

But now, here, at most all I ever feel is the urge to *see the world*, by which I mean leave the house, meet a friend for three beers, and then head home to sleep it off and try again tomorrow. *See the world*, I say, a world now reduced to something like the inn at the beginning of Kafka's *The Castle*. There's something Transylvanian about this place, something dungeon-y. The floor should be covered in straw, the barmaids should wear aprons tied high above the waist to accentuate their décolletage, the bartenders all bearded, like motorcyclists impersonating landlubber pirates, the jukebox pumping out immortal favorites of Joy Division, maybe a twelve-year-old track by the Flaming Lips, some Jimmy Smith on the soul groove organ.

I've spent thousands of dollars and hundreds of hours here. I've celebrated and suffered and everything in between at this bar with the worst possible cramped disgusting destroyed bathroom in town. Usually I don't worry about bathrooms, but this one, especially when the weather warms up, is notable. Its graffiti is the worst ever scrawl committed to bathroom walls, its tiny sink doubles as a urinal, its toilet is covered in stickers and seems like someone half succeeded in prying it from the floor, which is soggy from the overflowing sink and toilet, from vomit, urine, and unidentifiable effluvia. It's also possible that every night someone steps into this bathroom and their entire form liquefies and contributes to the sogginess. More than once I've seen customers at the bar near the toilet notice the smell and suggest they try another place or move to a table outside on the sidewalk. I'm glad I live nearby and will never have to rely on this bathroom in an emergency. In short, it's a terrible horrible disgusting bathroom, one I will excuse myself to visit several times tonight.

England and Snare should be here somewhere. Maybe Gibson and Oates too. It's hard to say when they'll show up. Unlike England and Snare, Gibson and Oates will leave their apartments early to see the world before they arrive, the world seen on the head of the pin known as this place, not a bad place at all. It's been the setting of so many Bloomsdays it would be sacrilegious not to celebrate here. Jonathan David Grooms will sense our familiarity with the environment and one another. He'll sense this is not the first time we've gathered to celebrate Bloomsday but also we've come here when there's nothing to celebrate or commiserate, the dark matter between galaxies, the random misty Tuesday night in March. Jonathan David Grooms will have every advantage over us except that of home field and numbers, that is, there will be one of him and many of us, our nameless little squadron, this team of practitioners of an art not so much cared for by anyone these days, like a team still together long after the league it plays in disbands.

I'll have the *Weihenstephaner Hefeweizen*, the unfiltered wheat beer from the self-proclaimed oldest brewery in the world, a brewery run by monks for nearly a thousand years. I can't think of a better beer for Bloomsday than the *Weihenstephaner Hefeweizen*. The most Irish-sounding draft selection would be the Sly Fox O'Reilly's Stout but the *Weihenstephaner Hefeweizen* is less a glass of beer than a glowing lemon-yellow scepter, plus the only regular Irish patron, an impish elfin housepainter, always smiling, unscrubbed, frazzled, with pierced ears and permastubble and a pack of Marlboro Reds in front of him, prefers the long tall glowing lemon-yellow scepter of *Weihenstephaner Hefeweizen* to the half-off American craft beers at happy hour. I prefer it too because it's unfiltered.

I want everything unfiltered. I want the natural cloudiness and density and goat-piss banana stench of the original *Weihenstephaner*

Hefeweizen recipe dating back to before the Black Plague, a *Weihen-stephaner Hefeweizen* in a tall and slightly tuliped toward the top *weizen* glass that makes for a head of creamy foam two to four fingers thick that doesn't settle, that clings to the tip of the nose, that leaves a trail of residue down the glass called *lacing* by beer blokes who rate every beer they drink in terms of the beer's presentation (appearance, smell, taste, mouthfeel) and the overall sense of it. The sense of sight, smell, taste, touch intact, but the sense of hearing could be replaced by the sound of the beer's name, the song that's heard when the beer's no more, the chance you'll hear yourself ask for another or something else, can more than one be had in a row, is the *mouthfeel* too much, the feel in the mouth unlike the taste on the tongue, awareness of underappreciated sensory experience.

Wine snobbery looks like well-conditioned cascades of blond hair smiling into a syrupy Riesling or some bald undersized persnickety anality frowning at an average Malbec, but today's beer blokery seems more like punk rocker biker types who in less urban areas would be outdoorsmen but here seem too blitzed to make it off the bar stool, thighs and ass and side-bellies thickened to stabilize the airy free-flow of fancy beer-induced thoughts, bearded heads not entirely connected to bodies after the third pint, T-shirts uniformly black and a little too tight and short in the back, forearms uniformly inked. About these men there's less of the artist than the explorer, the first round of beer blokes on ambitious quests to savor every iteration of every style of craft beer available in the United States if not the world, each beer a regional representative, each region understood by its representative breweries, the equivalent of contemporary baseball ballparks, the dream to drive around one day in a vintage conversion van and visit them all, the Dionysian urge to live a life made meaningful less by effort than enjoyment.

Oh how easy it'd be to become a dedicated beer bloke I think as my *Weihenstephaner Hefeweizen* arrives in a tall tuliped weizen glass, three fingers of creamy foam atop a lemon-yellow cloud of glowing carbonated goodness, refreshing, mildly intoxicating, 5% alcohol by volume, with scents and tastes of banana and spices, like ingesting the soft accommodating atmosphere of a perfect June day, its coolness and comfort, brightness and earth, immortal masterpiece of human ingenuity and industry, a drink enjoyed for a thousand years. All those human spirits eased, temporarily distracted by these glowing creamy-headed alchemical nectars, wheat and water transformed into liquid gold.

With one of these inside me I'll have the courage I need, *the vigor*, for Bloomsday, a city of spirits forming inside wherein I live another life in which I am an adventuresome beer bloke mountaineering an Everest of mild intoxication, communing with eras so remote I only imagine feudal misery overrun with free-range goat shit and toothless wenches and gruel of parsley and beets, the hooves and teeth of bony cows, a jar of fat left over from funeral pyres of deceased friends, straw always underfoot, wraiths terrorizing nights, all too worried about coal, never enough coal, hoarding coal beneath straw mattresses to ward off envelopment by cold, hoarding coal to heat the well water misty with sediment, fog capable of assuming human form, humans sprinting from crimes dissolve into fog that rises into the canopy of the surrounding forest, gnarled and lurching pines, the spiraling tar-black limbs of oaks leaning in and menacing anyone who dares enter on foot. On horseback it's different: a man's more than a man atop a horse, and after a sip of *Weihenstephaner Hefeweizen* I'm back in the saddle, elevated, head lightened, weight of world alleviated, the stress of work, writing work, imminent emergence of offspring, everything eases, chaotic bar scene harmonizes, jukebox pumps out a song about teenagers from Mars who don't care, everyone bops heads to it, an old favorite, a B-movie drive-in nostalgic rocker of adolescent alienation.

I angle past the jukebox and those standing holding pints behind those seated at the bar, past the infamous bathroom, and into a smaller squarer back room with two heavy wooden booths, each suitable for a Viking party of six, big blond-gray beards and bellies from sea to shining sea, enormous hands clasping flagons of churning golden liquid in which swim miniature sea dragons. There's also another longer narrower room with a dozen traditional two-person tabletops, sometimes pushed together, the walls adorned with neon lights and chalkboards with beer lists and dinner specials.

In the corner of the booth against the wall under the chalkboard draft list I see a familiar human form slouched over a mass-market paperback, its spine broken so the left-side pages curl behind those on the right. He's turned himself so most of his back is to the barroom. All I see is the rough pale skin of his neck, close-cropped hair darkened stiff with product, and an eye cocked like a lizard's to see what's behind him. He unfurls himself and gestures to sit opposite him in the Viking booth. I raise my alchemical scepter in a silent toast and slide all the way across what must be four seats, five if everyone squeezes in, and once I'm against the wall Kevin Snare squares his shoulders and lets me have it.

VII.

So after all that waffling, he says, you're here. Figured you'd wait to show, grand entrance and all, what with *Grooms* coming, and then he stomps the paperback with the meat of his fist.

I say *Grooms*.

He aggressively stretches the syllables, *Groom-zah-uh*.

I say *Bloomsday* and raise the most recent pour in a thousand-year succession of attempts by humans to beneficently poison themselves with creamy banana citrus nectar.

Snare tips an amber lager toward mine but we don't clink. He says *Groomsday*, when're *our days*, man?

It's clear he means it. If this is his baseline we're in for a night.

Snare says you ever read him?

I whisper of course, of course.

He says *of course, of course*, but you ever actually read this shit?

He pounds the cover of the mass market paperback: it's *Jonathan David Grooms vs. Jonathan Livingston Seagull*, Grooms's first novel about the famous short novel he read in sixth grade, an entire novel about JDG in college rereading *JLS* one day after his freshman year, documenting his thoughts, what he's doing, and how it relates and doesn't relate to the book. Somehow it works by all accounts. I haven't read it, since I try not to read Grooms. I said of course I'd read him but I've really only read a few essays and I own a few of his books, handled them this morning when we loaded our new shelves. I know how he writes and what he's written. I know his reputation and the reception of his novels but I've never really sat down to read his stories and major novels. If I read his stuff I'd sit down to my own work and have his sentences in my head, his style. I'd prefer not to doubt if what I write repositions his language, impersonates something he published.

Back when I was in Brooklyn, Grooms was at MacDowell, Yaddo, Millay, covert international writing retreats in the south of France and Italy and Romania and Slovenia and who knows where else, invited around the world to spend weeks and months to write. Writing retreats wanted to say Grooms had been there, slept there, wrote there, wanted his presence at meals, I imagine. By all accounts he's been a fixture on the international writing retreat circuit, off and on, for almost as many years as I've been writing, since I didn't write much in college. By the time I graduated Grooms had already published a story in the debut fiction slot in *The New Yorker*, a slot I hadn't even known existed at the time, and had published engaging memoir-infused cultural critiques in *Harper's*, a magazine I hadn't read much beyond the Index, all while I was only beginning to write imitations of canonical writers I admired.

At the time, just a blip ago really, less than twenty years ago, fifteen years ago even, Snare might have had some rosy fuzz on his pubis as he handed in sloppy handwritten synopses of novels assigned in intermediate school. He hadn't yet been hit by a car as he crossed the street one night near his parents' home in Northeast Philadelphia, hadn't yet been totaled by a hit and run at age twelve or thirteen. *An inch from my life* he always said as he held pincer fingers up with about a half inch between the tips. He always accompanied *an inch from my life* with this gesture suggesting how close he'd been to death, the phrase and gesture completed with a grimace, a pirate with skin of barnacle and salt remembering conflict with cannonball or crocodile, stating he hadn't so much lost a limb as he'd gained a peg.

All Snare's limbs remain intact but he seems arthritic for someone under thirty, his movements C3PO-ish, and despite successful
skin-grafting surgery something's still off about his right cheek. It's
a little smoother because it's been replaced with not entirely human
skin while the left side is naturally rough, as though without ever
coming an inch from his life when others were hoping to come an
inch from losing their virginity, without experiencing such an event
he would nevertheless have seemed descended from Irish stock intended to live hard lives on wind-whipped rocky coasts. I picture
Snare standing at the end of a jetty before a roiling sea, a pair of
lobsters in either hand, more like a fisherman off the Maine seacoast than anything Irish. But there remains a barnacled seafaring-
ness to him, something 21st century northeastern U.S. city life hasn't
scrubbed clean, and so with Snare more than most I sense a battle
between his nature and the natural world.

For centuries his people had adapted to their homeland and
then he found himself in Northeastern Philadelphia, one of the least
hospitable environments for human existence, or so Snare likes to
say, a sprawl of dilapidation, hell risen to the surface and smolder-
ing with visible flames of idiocy turning air into shimmery liquid,
unreal humidity oases ahead on midsummer highways, shimmery
idiocy through fissures in the blacktop of strip mall parking lots,
thin clear ribbons of ignorance and inconsiderateness, synonymous
with evil if not evil incarnate, flaming jets of off-brand natural gas
young Snare dreamed of igniting with the spark of an epigenetically
remembered Gaelic incantation accessible to him thanks to unen-
durably dull rehabilitation, years of it, something involving a staff
of interwoven serpents, pale yellow with human eyes, old country
magic replete with phallic imagery galore, generative when intoned
by elderly masters, destructive when stuttered as though improvised
by an adolescent at peace with intuitions of evil thanks to the hit and
run that proclaimed him a man, ushered him for good from the gar-

den of childhood into a wilderness overrun with prickers so sharp they threatened his every move, this adolescent at peace with intuition of a future at war with himself whenever he wondered what he might have been had he not been hit or had he never been born in this country, or at least raised somewhere other than Rising Sun Avenue.

He could have been raised along the Seacoast, somewhere ancestral souls centuries back may have recognized, external climate to match inner atmosphere, instead he attempts a pidgin Gaelic resembling Leprechaun-inflected German, nervous chattering slurred guttural English that, if reversed, would reveal satanic paganisms in inverted verb-subject-object syntax, strains of languages twining out of a Celtic core in a serpentine exhalation heavy on fricatives, light on plosives, a spark from the mouth of young Snare, a spark he sent into the night of an unnatural world that reeked of cracked gas mains sending narrow combustible filaments heavenward, noxious methanogenic squirminess embedded in the surface crap all around multiplied by thermogenic seepage from better adjusted lives, organic or not, buried forever beneath layer upon layer of permeable earth. He'd always thought he had some other sort of body meant for some other sort of place where the division of earth, water, and sky wasn't so obvious, but the hit and run made his surface seem one and the same with where he was. He'd thought when he looked in the mirror that his eyes were as yellow as the strip mall parking lot fluorescent overhead lamps not swarmed with mosquitoes and gnats because not even annoying winged insects survive the black hot heat rising from such expanses of exurban asphalt.

In another environment he might have been a woodsman in touch with the flora and fauna, in synch with ever-changing woods year round, friend of the chipmunk, unskeeved by maggots in fallen tree trunks, able to imitate the call of every wild animal for hundreds of acres all around, but instead the same sensitivity to the surrounding environment turned him into something as hard and as cracked as the parking lot asphalt. He was malleable and this combustible environment formed him into something no one really wanted to be. And so, in time, he found himself chanting made-up idiosyncratic Irish, hoping it would ignite the fissures of idiocy he envisioned streaming from cracks in parking lots and set off an all-consuming conflagration and reduce everything to ashes from which some gorgeous phoenix of a city might emerge, if not a Paris then a civilized French Quarter, a Beacon Hill, a colonial area lit with milky golden gas lamps, something rich and Dickensian and worth writing about, a place with characters not on obscure pharmaceuticals combing sidewalks for not quite empty littered nickel bags.

Ever since his licks of improvised idiosyncratic Irish failed to reduce his neighborhood to ashes he decided the war would have to be fought not out in the world but inside himself. The only thing he could save was himself, and he could only save himself by doing everything he could to get the hell out of there. Escape entailed staying inside strapped to an archaic dial-up computer, scanning for signs of civilized life, following pathways that led to a Catholic college in the city where he found himself, against his wishes, attracted to literature classes in general and writing in particular. Literature and writing weren't easy ways out but they seemed the most civilized, the most foreign to him as a child, and he never lost the feeling of power when he intoned his improvised Irish incantation and expected pervasive leaks of idiocy to explode as a result of his language, that the right combination of words released at the right time and place might destroy and reconstruct.

He essentially believed in immediately achievable magic, this pissed-off kid chronically sore and stiff who saw soreness and stiffness and perpetual pissed-offness everywhere around him, who wanted to crack the shell of hardened horribleness he perceived with a few good words. The destruction and gorgeous rebirth that crossed his mind as he intuitively intoned that lost Irish incantation spurred him to live another existence, if not on a rocky shore forever assaulted by churning wind and water then something warm, inviting, viscous, plasmatic, curative he'd cultivate with education, removal of self from streets, willful transformation into a ghost in the neighborhood, an egghead, stiff and hardened on the outside, gooey and generative on the inside. Everything from then on was intended to protect the yolk wherein who he wanted to one day be gestated, incubated, developed, evolved, until one day he knew if all went well he would shake off shell and spread wings and fly as high and as fast as he could from where he'd been fated to live, a place he had no say in selecting, a place he'd write about for the rest of his life as he tried as hard as he could to get the hell away from there.

Seeing him across the heavy wooden table of the Viking booth, pint in one hand, the other fist pounding Grooms's first novel, it's clear he's still in the shell of an ill-fitting world, considers publication of a first novel his emergence, the repeated pounding of the book the tapping of a baby bird's beak on the inside of his egg, a thousand more taps and everything will open and the publishing world will reveal itself as something more than the equivalence in intelligence of where he was raised.

It's all the same Snare might say apropos of nothing after the requisite intoxication takes hold, sweeping an arm above him to suggest a whirlwind of disappointment. He's worked as hard as anyone could work, he stayed in and worked, he wrote as much and as well as he could, read everything he could, studied everything, was accepted when he applied to the Iowa Writers' Workshop from an unknown yet rigorous temple of higher learning, Olney Catholic U., because a relatively successful Workshop graduate taught there and emailed notes to the director of the program at the time about this tough kid who walked with a limp and seemed to grimace when he moved but nevertheless would leave the library, arms loaded with books, all fiction, the young professor had said in notes to Frank Conroy. Good fiction, too, kid has spirit and talent and something else in there, wrote the young professor, an Irish American who at first published subtle tender poignant careful relationship-related literary fiction that succeeded critically (keyword commonality in reviews: "luminous") but no one really read, who then with the help of his young daughter conceived of a series of thrillers about the end of the world caused by a drastic increase in the number of vampires. The series fetched a seven-figure advance at auction and then went on to sell well and complicate his reputation, all of which happened a few years after he insisted that Snare *at least apply* to the Workshop and wrote a recommendation that appealed to the underdog Irish-American side in old man Conroy, someone who always took a chance on a few students a year who didn't come from Brooklyn/Manhattan, the Ivy League, Chicago, San Francisco, Stanford, Los Angeles.

Every year he admitted a percentage of kids who seemed to harbor something that couldn't be denied, whose work demonstrated *an intelligence that pulsed through the page* he'd said, and so Snare caught an early break thanks to Frank Conroy's interest in *protecting the edge*, he'd said, or so I'd heard, Frank Conroy, director of the Workshop, careful to admit applicants his intuition suggested might have something special that needs coaxing, needs to swim in the same pool as graduates of Harvard and Yale, Brown and Columbia and Cornell, Oberlin, Wesleyan, Vassar, and the like, Frank Conroy protecting the edge from which he'd come. Before he attended one of those suburban Philadelphia liberal arts colleges that sound like cagey aristocrats, Lord Swarthmore and Duchess Haverford, he'd come from New York City and Florida squalor and never lost that feeling in his gut, and though he wanted the association with conventional excellence he also needed to rebel against it and let contemporary underdog iterations of himself into the Workshop.

I've always pictured Snare stiff and limping and saying *oh jeez* a lot as he took the winding cobblestone path up a slight hill to where the Workshop sat in all its Victorian gingerbread splendor. Inside it were all these writer elves, I've always thought, kids from Ivy League schools, top liberal arts colleges, top progressive liberal arts colleges, and a smattering of outliers, all in black leather shoes and black-framed glasses, everyone wearing denim overalls for some reason, sexy in a librarian sense, I've always imagined, elfin if shapely and svelte, gnomish if lumpy, frumpy, particularly formed, all sitting at one long heavy wooden drawing board-like table, or so I've always pictured it, like at a beer garden or Iroquois longhouse. Younger writers wrote away while older professional writers, Pulitzer Prize winners, O. Henry Award winners, Pushcart winners, National Book Award winners walked in lazy intimidating cryptical elliptical loops around the table, surveying works in progress, whispering encouragement in a diffident writer's ear, undermining the excessive undeserved confidence of another, calling for a pause so something brilliant just composed could be read aloud and savored and emulated but not blindly copied or satirized, before a bell was rung by an energetic administrative assistant at a certain hour whereupon the writers of the Workshop would break for cigarettes, coffee, and booze, before starting the day's second session in which what they wrote in the morning underwent editorial evisceration at the hands of each writer's neighbor to the right, red pens ablaze across the morning's composition, all the typos, the cuteness, the indulgence, the opacities, the abstractions, the stock descriptions, the sensory deprivations, the spirited individualism, the run-on sentences attacked to the point of annihilation, unruliness and ranginess be damned, the long table textured with the scars of sadistic editing sessions.

I've always imagined Snare seven or so years younger, ready for his first workshop session, ready to wow 'em, this kid from North Philadelphia's Olney Catholic U., one side of his face smoother than the other, with stiff movements, almost like the Tin Man when really feeling sore. I see the kid limp in, one leg not quite as long as the other, this uneven urban kid with a pirate-like facial tic, one eye closed and the other open wide as he yawns the silent barbaric yawp of a newborn, a stranger in a strange land that runs on smart young men and women writing fiction. Somehow a place like this actually exists and has existed for seventy-five-plus years, a proven track record of success, a history of esteemed graduates, and then there's Snare, first-year fictionist from Northeast Philadelphia, overwhelmed with the foresight of inevitable triumph, wearing white leather sneakers, pale denim jeans a little short at the cuff, plush new midnight-green sweatshirt emblazoned with the official logo of the Philadelphia Eagles football franchise, the aerodynamic aggressive curve of the beak a talisman for young Snare, the talons out of sight but he imagines them ripping into fellow students from Harvard and Yale, he imagines bloodying them with incisors and fingernails and pencils and pens, feeding on their soft flesh. Inside the gingerbread Victorian placed upon the slightest incline they call a "hill" in a little college town in eastern Iowa they call a "city," the long Workshop table assumes the form of a feeding trough for this northeastern parochially educated animal with sharp teeth and claws and aspirations to one day achieve a sort of eaglehood, to sprout wings and talons and razor beak and soar high above and swoop upon whosoever deserves a smackdown.

Snare, a Philadelphia Eagle extraordinaire, a combination of the team's legendary free safety Brian Dawkins and an actual raptor-like eagle and a handful of writers he admires (Vonnegut, Hemingway), his first session was not a calming helpful respectful exercise in constructive criticism but a slaughter, butchery pure and simple. *Snare oh Snare what have you done?* he says to himself when it turns out the table hath turned, the tide of bloodlust. Triumph foreseen revealed as mindless bravado he'd mustered to make it up the hill and push open the heavy gingerbread doors of the Workshop and sit at that long table, knowing deep down that no matter how much he wanted to sit there and be welcomed and feel as though he belonged his natural hostility to feeling welcomed and made to feel like he belonged undercut any possibility of feeling welcomed and made to feel like he belonged. So once turbulence started he assumed crash position, ducked and covered and hoped not for triumph but something more like survival, a landing no matter how rough, a beer or two or ten later, however many it took to restore humbled wings and talons and beak. Even Frank Conroy, the one who protected the edge, found himself agreeing with student consensus, lapping up the red pen marks, savoring the good clean iron of it, the faint hot pepper spice of fear, of terror, of hormones released by an animal tortured before the death blow. The second-year students in particular displayed murderous capacities, sadistic abilities, or so I've always imagined from stories heard about these initial workshop sessions from Snare, from England, from Gibson, from Oates.

The first few times I hung out with these guys, after meeting them at a reading Guardian had hosted, the air clouded over with war stories of great Workshop battles they'd survived. After they'd quaffed enough they seemed to cultivate something that made them seem like veterans of a two-year stint in some rogue Midwestern republic declaring independence from the nation, an enclave in the heart of the country's heartland, a miniature Midwestern American take on Lesotho or, better yet, a self-proclaimed literary elite version of Vatican City. They'd returned from active duty in Iowa City, surrounded on all sides by corn and soy and blond descendants of Swedish and Czech immigrants, territories flattened by glaciers and wind sweeping across the prairie until in eastern Iowa the earth undulates like a slowly snapping flag, a series of easily conquered hills, consistent lumps undaunted by Big Sky and the enormity of infinitely upward night, and once they achieved extreme quaffage they revealed their battle scars.

Remember that time Frank ripped whoever a new one and said there wasn't a drop of *the milk of human kindness* in her characters. Remember that night at the Foxhead when whoever got trounced that afternoon threw the cue ball off the pool table at the bathroom door after someone who'd ripped him went in there, splintering it. These great battles that raged in the literary enclave equivalent of Vatican City, how Snare had it out for two second-year students who'd taunted him. The apparently weakest writers in the second year attacked Snare early on in his first year, scoffed at him and flaunted their mannered superiority, their Midwestern state school college-boy affectations of world weariness that Snare wanted to feed on like a hungry attack dog riled up, directed to kill upon release, Snare holding himself back, sneering at the figurative choke chain around his neck, knowing what might happen if he let himself go, if he let himself slip the collar he long ago knew he had to wear to distance himself from everyone around him. Where he'd grown up was more than enough to fuel instantaneous obliteration of these smug no talent fucks who entered a room teeth-first shaggy hair and slouchy false timidity.

Self-conceiving for the first time as *Fucking Snare*, his first name transformed to an active expletive, the anger in him all-consuming and if ever unleashed *man oh man* but he'd said to himself it was ammunition reserved for the page. They ripped his first story because he'd submitted something for ritual sacrifice that wasn't made of fire and so it burst into flames when students set it alight. From then on after initial immolation of enthusiasm for writing and by extension enthusiasm for life, once he regained confidence and shook off humility arising as a consequence of universal denouncement, even from Frank (Snare later discovered this was common) and from fellow first-year student John England (who Snare said was quietly critical of everyone's stories but wrote three pages of surprisingly helpful single-spaced comments and line-edited all manuscripts with suggestions for tightening/improvements), who tried to be nice about Snare's first offering and revive the corpse as an exercise in revision and resurrection, once Snare recovered he would only dip his pen in the hot oil reserve that simmered and bubbled and threatened at all times to take the place of his blood, that hot black flammable sludge inside him he would externalize in stories, thereafter he would only produce something already in flames and able therefore to resist the flamethrowers of fellow students.

Vesuvius Snare, Snare St. Helens, Snare at war with conservatory fiction, predictable poignancy, privileged hand-wringing about the consequences of a decision made long ago. He hadn't made a decision to step into a street that hadn't seemed occupied by a car that turned a corner looking left for oncoming traffic as it accelerated to the right and plowed through adolescent Snare, lifting him across the hood *god bless* instead of pushing him under for the wheels to break what remained unbroken by impact with an American muscle car, its grill like the head of a chrome shark. Somehow he landed on his side and thanks to adrenaline energizing the elasticity of youth pulled himself to the side of the road and there he figured he would die. Too aware of the presence of his skeleton at too young an age, forever after aware of a fragile structure, of bones instead of the surface of his skin and strengthening muscle. Snare radicalized by that first Workshop, not realizing it until later he had been reborn from ashes not as anything mythological, anything fictional, but as a soldier, a fighter on illusory battlefields, waging wars of words to save the souls of those unaware there's even a war, a samurai loyal only to the accurate energetic portrayal of unseen wars. Unlike wars in central Africa or the Balkans that make the news but otherwise don't seem to affect those in the West, he would accurately and energetically portray unseen wars in the hearts and minds and bodies of Americans, struggles like those he'd won when he restrained himself from bursting through those smug second-year fucks. Had he let himself burst through them he wouldn't have the energy to write what he'd been writing the past few years, what he'd finished recently, what he wouldn't let me see, what he'd only let John England see, what his future and the past few years and his marriage to a forgiving pediatric oncology nurse were based on, this gamble he didn't see as a gamble because he had already won, all bets off.

What he'd written could not be *not* published, could not *not* receive attention from agents and editors because he wrote with the hot black oil reserve in his body instead of old-fashioned conventional ink. Two years at the Workshop radicalized young Snare but now seven years later he's somehow thirty and all he has is this novel manuscript he wrote when he wasn't teaching at his alma mater Olney Catholic U., this novel England won't talk about when I ask him to describe it. He says it's *pure Snare* and seems daunted not so much by the book but by my interest in it, as though it were secret battle plans for the aggressive expansion of Snare's position in the world. Evasion about Snare's manuscript makes me unsure if Snare's insane or onto something, has written something he'll get Grooms to read and Grooms will force his publisher to print under the stipulations of his contract. It's clear that Snare's conflicted because he clearly wants to win Grooms over and gain an influential ally but he isn't sure based on the little he's read that doing so won't undermine everything he's worked on over the past seven years, every radicalized pose of self-reliant high-minded extremism with regard to calling bullshit on everything overhyped.

As well as he possibly could he called bullshit on consecutive high-profile Pulitzer Prize winners and called bullshit on any number of hyped debuts that all shared the fault of not relating directly to the literary career of Kevin Snare. I loved that he'd called bullshit on these books since it kept me from reading them. I outsourced my bile to Snare when it came to these books and read his takedowns with glee, thanks to the sense that Snare allowed something true inside him to emerge, the language squirming and alive, throbbing with a sense of righting a wrong. There was an urgency to his calls to arms. They read like battle cries, the literary equivalent of ululation, running through the streets setting fire to the houses of those in power. I guess you could reduce Snare to a term like *firebrand*, but there's something about him that was terribly hurt at a formative age and he dedicated his life to righting that insult on abstract artistic levels. Engaging these battles, he signed himself up for a lifetime of struggle, fighting the same fights, defending all that might be vanquished by the amalgamated forces of idiocy, but still he soldiers on, our Snare.

VIII.

So how's your *Snaresday* been, I say.

Good, man, good, he says. Great being down here again. Been trying to talk Allison into moving into the city but she needs a lawn and, come to think of it, so do I.

Here's lawn enough for me, I say as I raise my hefeweizen.

Snare says everyone's late.

Everyone's bailed, I say.

Snare says see how he's screwed Bloomsday.

Did you finally read it?

Snare says *Ulysses*? That's not the point.

What then?

Snare says *this*, and he taps the table with his pint.

Mano a mano, mi hermano, I say.

Snare says where's England, Gibson, Oates?

I say how's your thing coming, any bites? (I know how to interest Snare.)

No news isn't good news, he says. I mean, why can't they drop everything and say 'thank you for sending your novel manuscript, I am thankful to have been selected to have the opportunity to read your work and with pleasure I hereby extend an offer to sell it to the highest bidder,' or at least they could say 'sorry I read the first pages and skimmed another twenty and don't think this will work for me, better luck elsewhere.' They could say something simple and polite in days instead of weeks or months.

I say it's always months for me.

VIII.

Snare says there's something wrong if you can't complete a manuscript and send it to an agent and see it in a bookstore in a month.
Instead you work on a novel for seven years and after going over and
over it, you take out a comma and put it back in, say it's done, send
it out, and then nothing, silence, *nada*, zip.

I say the world could give a shit.

Snare says the world could definitely give more shits.

There's no way Snare will ask about what I'm working on, if I'm
getting any bites as Guardian likes to say, like we're casting baited
hooks into a pond and waiting for lax lines to tighten and pull in an
agent and a book deal and a transformed life.

Life transformed after I moved to Philadelphia, or really, after
I met my wife. We pooled our savings (hers more than mine) and
bought a rowhome that needed minimal work, that had a view of
the complete western sky from a roof deck, that had a little concrete
patio out back where we evolved a modest flower garden in plastic
buckets we painted bright colors, the cinder block walls out back we
painted bright blue, too, the little concrete area out back in summer
vibrating with greenery and light, enough life for anyone, enough
room for anyone, and of course the comfort of marriage, the consis-
tency of it.

A few years out of college, relationships would perish under the
specter of marriage: would I pledge to live with this person till death
did us et cetera, would I want to face this face every morning for
the next five or six or fifty or sixty years, would I mingle my helices
with her helices and collaborate on the creation of a good citizen in
the form of our entwined helices, and is this sort of productivity not
in some way *reprehensible* compared to productivity that hopes to express itself one day as a published novel?

Is it right to make more people on a planet with so many people it's possible that the collective weight of their bodies plus their
houses, cars, desks, bookcases, et cetera, weighs down the world to

such an extent that there may soon be three hundred and sixty-*six* days per year, Earth's orbit slowed thanks to all the people and their stuff, tacking on another day, perhaps a holiday celebrated world-wide during which citizens of the world lighten loads, reduce, reuse, recycle, and so *is it right* to bring another person into a world so encumbered by humanity that it's ever so surely slowing down? Another human being brought into this world would not correct the pace, plus bringing a new human into the world would distract from bringing *novel manuscripts* into the world, from contributing to the weight of the world in the form of trade hardbacks all over North America, the United Kingdom, Germany, Italy, Spain, maybe even France, Portugal, and then the paperback editions, all that paper spread out all over the world, weighing it down, or at least weighing down the more literate territories and territories in which literate types travel.

I can't remember where I read about the additional day. It may have been a story by Lao Guardian. Sounds like something he might write, parodying news about global catastrophe derived from exaggeration of a misreading of an abstract of a complicated scientific study. That sort of thing's up Lao's alley, phrased in his patented exaggeration of passive voice, that is, *the voice of passivity that was phrased to the point of exaggeration* and therefore characteristic of the marks his paper received from his pen. I worry about my memory, especially when it fuzzes thanks to three quarters of a glass of 4.5% ABV hefeweizen.

All the time I've been thinking about the weight of the world my friend Snare here has been talking about how the world could give a shit about what he's working on. He lists everything the world gives a shit about more than it gives a shit about his novel. He continues along these lines, the beer loosening his tongue, the reward center in his brain dreaming of Hall of Fame worthiness when it comes to big league literary fiction.

Yes, another glorious scepter of *Weihenstephaner Hefeweizen* for me, please, and once I order I wonder if I should tell Snare about the pregnancy. I haven't seen him in months and he might not have heard. I know that Snare and his wife have no interest in reproduction, not for moral reasons but because Allison devotes everything she has to sick kids, all day every day surrounded by them. Some can't be saved by anything other than miraculous intervention but she doesn't believe much in a higher power because why would a higher power bring these children into the world only to take them out at the cellular level, slowly, painfully? So she doesn't want children, plus Snare seems, more than his spouse, against the idea of children in general, as entities, as occupants of small, precious, overly protected, oohed-and-ahhed-over portions of the planet.

It's all a trap, he says when questioned about children. He's considered typing and printing his response, having it ready in his wallet, a laminated list of reasons he's not interested in having children. Atop this list is writing. Children and writing are mutually exclusive. How can anyone think about what they're working on when consistently confronted with a little baby? Why bother making more people if it gets in the way of making more books? And then what if the kid you spend all that time and effort and money raising doesn't become a reader? What if despite attempts to indoctrinate the child into the cult of reading the kid's a philistine twit who overintellectualizes mainstream conventional literary fiction and misuses multisyllabic words? What if the kid has dyslexia or attention deficit disorder? What if it's a savant when it comes to high-tech high-def video games wherein one kills soldiers in war-torn cyber environments studded with civilians dressed for work, picking flowers, strolling unconcerned as soldiers sprint around spraying ammunition at low-flying helicopters and snipers and various anxious assailants?

What if the child's a metaphorical civilian unaware of the battle raging all around, ammunition spent daily on the shattered busted bullet-riddled stages on which soldiers like Kevin Snare engage the lit world in a King of the Mountain struggle to keep at it, not quit, not listen to anything other than tightening in the chest that says *proceed*, put head down and fight, engage, carry off the dead and lick wounds and heal and rest and read and prepare for battles to come?

Keep at it, string another phrase ahead of the last. The need to keep at it similar to the need to stay alive, keep heart beating, fill space with text, fill lungs with breath, type to assert a presence animated by an intelligence motivated to make a difference when it comes to the world of books and the worlds *within* books, not physical objects/products but compendiums of expressions of what it's like to be alive.

All these books out there not for entertainment purposes, all these books do more than entertain, so what if your soldiering existence is undermined by a child destined to exist as a civilian oblivious to the existence of the war itself? Without a little luck the child may never know that places without GPS coordinates exist. All the lessons Snare would have to teach, I will have to teach, coax from the child, an understanding developed over time so for the first decade it's fantasy and emerges in the second decade as something more than reality. Oh but the kid could happily live a life fulfilled thanks to not wanting much, and maybe that would be better than wanting something the world rarely provides.

Snare wonders where England is and sends him a text.

IX.

Snare and England found each other at grad school and fused at the shoulder. Snare and England, England and Snare, deemed interchangeable, rarely referred to as solo entities, the way Snare and I are solo entities in this Viking booth, our state endangered with England en route. England's not someone with children or a child on the way, no girlfriend, taking a break from online dating to work on his book, he says, abstaining to write but also maybe taking some time to transform himself? There's something about England that's difficult to finger, something stunted that keeps him from seeming more generative, like a lid atop a fire in his loins maybe related to a desire to do it with men? But England resembles a fireplug too much to imagine it, fingers thick in a way that suggests the rest of him, that makes it difficult to imagine him in particular with Snare. Slow-mo tackling, sweaty wrestling lacking technique other than flex and clench. Silent yet violent asphyxiation of hamster by snake. Tender battle more than love fest and then they go for burgers and beers and talk football and books as they wash the taste out of their mouths.

It's possible something of the sort has been going on for years and no one's expected it since they're buddies, chums, dudes who enjoy each other's company, nothing more than that. I don't see why any more must be made of it, England would say, agitated, tapping the table, a cat snapping its tail. If he's good at anything he's good at tamping down irritation, holding his tongue. Of all the things he could have been good at, he's best at restraint.

Generally, among us all, I would vote him most likely to have his visage carved into the side of a remote cliff, eyes closed yet turned at a forty-five degree angle toward the sun as it drops. The face of an American man of Western European descent accepting elemental forces as though the visage carved into the remote mount is punishment more than eternal reward. Face turned to the heavens forever undergoing water torture, winds plunging from northern tundra, a scythe of air and ice, freezing at night, baked all day, the cycle of light and darkness a fever dream. Mount England, remote rockface portrait of magnanimous author and man, forever dreaming about the country, about his place in it, about his publication history, about achievement of bourgeois respectability through the unreliable transit of literary fiction. England, teacher of composition and fiction, not yet carved into a Dakotan cliff, needs a published novel or collection of stories to take the next step in his career as a professor. All he seems to think about is how a publication of merit will improve his standing in higher education.

Once he had wanted to write and publish but now he *needs* to write and publish. The history of the world, per *War and Peace*, may be the history of necessity but, when it comes to writing, when one hasn't yet written something that someone else has wanted to publish, the noise of professional necessity is not so good. There's urgency to publish to secure a better academic position, ideally after securing an agent who secures a book deal and then there's more money and the sort of publishing credit that departments of creative writing like to see on the curriculum vitae of applicants to creative writing jobs.

I will never experience a situation of the sort because my writing has nothing to do with my work. In no way will selling a novel improve my standing at work. Publication of my office novel in progress may even diminish my standing in the office if word gets out I've written a book based on dynamics encountered in my office, might undermine my efforts to work in such a way that I never think about work at night or weekends when home other than when writing about an alternate-reality workspace filled with alternate-reality colleagues, something I started with urgency once we learned a baby was on the way, a life of consistent work at home, consistently fed by life at work in the office.

I need to write this office novel because otherwise I fear daily office life may *kill me*, an exaggeration because there's no way sitting all day at a computer with two large beautiful monitors and a swift keyboard ever killed anyone. It's that my one precious existence may be wasted at a computer in an office setting, working with an ever-changing cast of colleagues in only five years at this office, a meaningless existence on the face of it. The office novel I've been working on therefore fights for the significance of everyone's existence there, even if I am not always a fan of most people I work with during the bulk of the hours we share awake. But even *that* seems like something that requires some urgency, necessity, to justify our existence, to find meaning therein, whatever "meaning" means, my colleagues never seeming to wonder what "meaning" means when it comes to existence in our office, although of course they may walk by me as I work and think I never think about the meaning of "meaning," never think about the meaning of life if most of our life together means working in this office.

There's an urgency to what I write, I think, because if I didn't write it or if I wrote about something unrelated to work life, my life may be endangered if I worked only to make a living and pay for nights at home, a place to sleep, savings, security, good food and better drink, not to mention health care for pregnant unemployed wife and imminent birth and everything thereafter, all the clothes and meals, but also I work to afford a place to store the books I buy. I primarily work to afford the *ad libitum* acquisition of books. I primarily work to afford a place to write a book about work as I read writing that burst from the skulls of authors once a subject or a scenario or an alternate reality based on an experience of reality made its way to manuscript pages with enough urgency to find a publisher and stay published or at least not be pulped and therefore find its way to the sanctuary of my shelves.

It's a parental instinct, a protective one, to feel like I need to save the lives of myself and my colleagues, to rescue good books and place them next to their kin on my shelves. In no way do I feel like this is pathological. Some may deem it pathetic to salvage this dreary stuff but I've always thought of it as urgent preservation of the perishable.

I write to preserve the perishable. So I need no validation other than the act. To look over the progress I've made in the act of preserving the perishable and see that the vital present has been represented in a way that will exist in text as long as I'm alive, and if I infect my child or children with the reading virus these preservations may even survive into the future. That's the worst case scenario.

The worst case scenario is that what I write exists as long as I live, is read by me and maybe a few others over the next few dozen years at most and then disappears. Or it's passed onto offspring who keep it aloft a while more. Or it goes online and is lost there. Or it's published and dispersed and then lost forever. Or it's published, dispersed, translated, becomes part of the culture before it's forgotten. Or it's published, dispersed, translated, becomes part of the culture, quoted, remembered, returned to, recognized as something in which a sense of vital urgency that once existed remains accessible and urgent, necessity that once compelled its creation remains necessary, the spark of conception remains in the text and transfixes readers who are infected by its necessity and urgency and their lives seem necessary and urgent even if nothing much happens to them of note, nothing dramatic, nothing very much in conflict, and yet even then the conflict is between urgent necessity and unnecessary existence, unrelated to professional standing and attainment of bourgeois respectability better achieved through a sales or managerial position, and so, at best, in sum and in short, at my most generous, I picture England with eyes almost shut, his unprotected face upturned to the elements as they stream down from the northwest.

A long lost cousin of Mount Rushmore, I hope Mount England endures the elements, as patient as limestone or shale or whatever rock they use to carve visages. He's having trouble with the requisite patience of course but also the correct generative instinct, what I would call the *correct generative instinct*. When England or anyone else starts talking about publishing for the sake of their career as teachers of creative writing, I don't rant about *correct generative instinct* because there's no way they'll listen to me because they're certified creative writers, certified fiction writers, certified *masters of fine arts* released into universities that hire *masters of fine arts* in creative writing with a specialization in fiction to teach composition classes and creative writing workshops. At first not paying much and not providing benefits and then paying a little more and providing benefits but not providing job security, even if these employees have secured *masters of fine arts* in creative writing with a specialization in fiction from top-ranked programs and the department chairs within the universities brag about how they've hired these *masters of fine arts* from the top-ranked programs to teach in their departments for low pay and no benefits at first, thrown into classrooms to instruct kids at most interested in attaining an easy A, at worst misbehaving students, students who rarely show up, stoned entitled students, students with odd ideas about what's acceptable to do or say in class. These *masters of fine arts*, these fine artists certified in creative writing/fiction, in turn spend after-class hours complaining about students, rehashing horrors instead of honoring promising students or airing anything they'd learned about writing via talking all day about writing with students. Instead they harp on the worst possible students as they sit in bars and rant about their students.

I look to my left toward the door and expect to see England slide into our booth, face blue, lips purple, eyes red, fingers contorted as he crumples in on himself, deflated, so concerned about publishing he's cut off requisite oxygen to the brain, eternally light-headed, unable to process information or move with much grace, at least not until he has a drink and airways reopen and tension releases as he enters the eternal present of this Transylvanian barroom inn specializing in the fanciest beers on the planet, the eternal present of the one hundred and eighth anniversary of Bloomsday when Joyce reanimated in once-modern quotidian Dublin occurrences originating in the mythopoetic Mediterranean. Now it's the same day if you want it to be, a day on which England isn't England as he usually is but England as he'd been, the England of antiquity, happy-go-lucky kid with thin blond hair tearing up Portland area tennis courts, soccer fields, applying to conservative East Coast colleges because his parents were East Coast conservatives and envisioned their son at one of those schools, especially in Maryland, where England's parents met after his father had finished the Naval Academy and married to ensure the father had someone to return to when he emerged from beneath the surface of the sea.

I watched movies like "The Hunt for Red October" as a kid but England's father lived that life, in dark war-machine capsules lit by strings of red neon along ceiling and floor, chasing a rogue sub captained by Crazy Ivan or whatever covert missions he went on, ready to launch on those pesky Ruskies and dive at max torque in opposite direction toward accommodating trench to wait out the worst first days of nuclear winter. If all went well it'd be one-sided, the brouhaha about mutually assured destruction oversold. We sneak a shot and incapacitate launch mechanisms and territories once temporarily conquered by Napoleon are *flambéed aux champignons*, and meanwhile all submarine occupants wonder if their families will survive as they surface off the Tahitian coast and expect to see what the first Euro explorers saw there, islanders so affable, men accommodating, women alluring, sunbursts over distant midwinter tundra expressed in tropical flora, original island paradise, a good place to start over once they murder all the men in their sleep.

England could always hit reset if the whole writing thing didn't work out. Start over, forget about a decade or so dedicated to writing and teaching and instead wait tables again or take an editorial office job and otherwise release himself from the tyrannous pressure of trying to write publishable fiction. He never said this to me or Snare as far as I know but there's always been this sense that he'd love to return to soccer fields outside Portland, Mt. Hood in the distance, when he had longish stringy sweaty blond hair and took his youth for granted and wanted more than anything to become an adult. Now he either wants the future or the distant past, or some alt-reality in which his father ended the world and restarted things best he could on an island of smiling floral women, without remorse or thoughts of avenging the slaughter of husbands and sons, these islanders always existing in an eternal present otherwise known as paradise. England wanted something like that and instead was en route to sit for hours with us and battle.

I picture him chewing his thumbnail as he walks to the bar, as Snare and I survey our phones, and then here he is: England in the flesh, not blue, not purple lipped, not red eyed. He seems healthy and sun-kissed. His shins reflect the recessed lighting in a way that radiates excessive sheen, like he shaved and waxed and moisturized his shins to seem comely in shorts ending above the knee. England has *good knees*, strong tennis- and soccer-playing suburban legs accentuated by little white socks and slip-on canvas sneakers. He wears a short-sleeved collared shirt with a logo on the left breast of a man with a mallet in the air astride a charging horse, a nonconformist choice in context where most men wear black T-shirts and jeans. His shirt clings to his thick broad torso, his shoulders rounded and strong, like his strong and steady fiction.

England's writing goes for the heart and gut. It channels Tobias Woolf and Tim O'Brien as it updates Richard Yates and Richard Ford and Richard Russo and Richard Bausch. His writing seems born from the era of the Great American Richards, the hunting trips with fathers described by the Great American Richards, the stoic iceberg thing the Great American Richards specialized in, the tip suggesting the rest unseen, the crafty magic trick the Great American Richards perfected, nothing too mystical about it, the pineal gland numbed by drink and sorrow. It's anti-ecstatic work, attentive, crafty, at peace with traditional narrative pathways, rising arc, realization, resolution, sentences knitted and stitched in such a way a sensitive reader might pull a thread and feel the story unravel as a string is pulled in the reader's heart, these Richards always hunting hearts.

John England, hunter of hearts, out there on the savannah where elevated expectations meet dashed dreams, affably unprepared and bumbling but someone you root for, armed with a quiver of tears and a light, flexible, simple bow like one used by an elfin warrior prince in a story a Richard would never write. Everything about these Richards hunting reader hearts unlike big-game archers using infrared night goggles and laser rangefinder tucked in neoprene camouflage case and bow like a handheld suspension bridge complete with high-tension pulley system, the muscles in the backs of these archers attuned to their enthusiasm for shooting arrows at circles on wood or paper or the vitals of a black bear, a moose, a proud buck traipsing across alpine terrain, and then from six hundred yards upon tension and release the buck or bear falls and the archer knives out the heart and squeezes it into an iron cup to steam in the brisk autumn air before he drinks it down.

Great American Richards comparatively are not quite at one with nature but natural in the sense that they're stumbling men, get-

ting away from life and wife and everything in pursuit, the game becomes the hunter, the goal of the hunt a symbolic parallel, the buck
representing something feral in the Richard's nature, something
that must be conquered, something the Richard wants to let be. Thus
there's conflict, that old Faulknerian nugget about *the heart in conflict
with itself* upon which Richards thrive, feast on, their bread and butter inner conflict related to man against nature, man against society, man against expectations and conventions, and so with nothing
more than a light bow handed down from a great-grandfather who
took it off a Chinook tribesman found lying by the side of a remote
footpath when the great-grandfather was lost in the woods and the
bow saved his life, with this same bow the Richard otherwise always
at a loss these days hunts and returns to his one true self, the deep
masculine self his predecessors knew. For once he can access it, that
original force, the psychic musculature of the hunt, the slow careful
steps and precise silent movements, a pantomime except now it's
real.

Hand reaches over shoulder and extracts arrow and feeds groove
at feathered end into gut-wire that spans the bow, one arm extends
and the other retracts and at that moment Richards are primed to
overcome all thoughts about fathers, all thoughts about mothers,
all thoughts about wives and children, all thoughts about anything
as though primed and ready to strike is the essential way of being,
as though *thought* about anything is affliction, all stories wiped of
thoughts, cleansed of ideas, the only thoughts and ideas present in
the stories are suggestions of thoughts and ideas. Stories are not the
home of ideas, they say, the mind not at home in the world these stories relate. Richards go after heart and gut, the primary organ and
the lower organs, not the highest organ, at most something in the
language triggers a tingle at the top of the spine, a *frisson*, something
where brain meets body without warning goes on high alert, but
that's the extent of the brain work, the central nervous system an en-

emy to overcome with drink and the hunt, a car pressed to its limits on the highway at night, speeding no one knows where, headlights casting an ominous strobe across feathery pines leaning in along the shoulder-less road.

England is a John, not a Richard, but he's a practitioner of the noble strand of American Literary Fiction known as minimalist stories about sad sack men who for a moment sense former vigor they thought forever lost. At a time in my reading life I wasn't able to deal with Richard stories encountered in academic literary journals (state name followed by the word "review"), collected each year in the *Best American Short Stories*. When I was younger there was no way such stories were for me. I felt pressure to write such stories even if they had nothing to do with how I'd been raised or how I'd lived my life. I wasn't an alcoholic, I wasn't divorced, I didn't hunt, I'd done well enough in school (other than math and science classes), I'd played some sports and did pretty well, I'd had adequate luck with girls and, later, with women, and since I wasn't an alcoholic hunter I didn't have weapons lying around my apartment that could be introduced in the second act so they'd go off in the fifth.

All in all these Richard stories were like the ones about the forces of good struggling with the forces of evil for control of the one ring of power, all set somewhere called Middle Earth, an alternate history that paralleled what I knew at the time of World War II, the struggle between Axis and Allies for control of the A-bomb. I preferred the elaborate imaginative slant to stoic stories involving fathers and sons on the hunt. But when older I was able to see these Richard stories as allegories similar to Tolkien's, not so much about what they seemed to be about, potentially applicable to anyone's life, since everyone has a father or a father figure or a shadowy sense of something that's like a father in one's life, and everyone is a son, even if they're a daughter, and everyone has something to hunt, and everyone knows what it's like to feel the bow stretched back ready to release and do something exhilarating that won't necessarily feel good and won't come without substantial conflict thereafter either, and so when I read England's stuff I respect the tradition he's working in and admire it, and I also know these Richard stories aren't necessarily hunting me.

The readers they're hunting live out west. They're probably dead now but when the Richards were in their prime, the readers they hunted were a couple who lived on a small farm. They were a little older than the authors, in their late fifties, not so limber anymore but lean and aware, and at night they read their favorite Richard stories aloud and recorded them on an old-fashioned cassette in a battery-operated tape deck, nothing special, and late afternoons when they rode out on their tractor to a back acre near the little pond they had out there that was radiant and pungent and alive in different ways throughout the season, they packed themselves a simple meal and sat on their tractor when the weather was amenable and played their cassette recording. Richards always envisioned this couple out on a modest ranch in Montana or Wyoming, having a simple meal, listening to the tapes of the stories they'd made. These Richards envisioned open space and straightforward talk and *a bright-shining horizon* toward which these stories headed as the Richards at all times reassured their ideal western readers that life had significance, the accumulation of sentences matched that of days, each on its own a poem layered atop the last, an accretion of meaning, streaming with discrete inexact significance from one to the next, leading toward *a bright-shining horizon* that the Richards imagined the readers they hunted saw every evening as the sun dropped. The Richards wanted their apparently straightforward and accessible stories to move toward this light at the end, not a goal or destination but a sense that the sentences of life, like units of time, are shepherded, shown safe passage, through the pages to come.

A beautiful image perfumed with outdoorsy sights and sounds, the down-to-earth Author God gracefully meeting readers halfway along the arc of energy between writers and readers, a narrative covenant suggesting never will we Richards play post-modern metafictional referential intertextual mindfuck games to make you feel alienated and dumb. The narrative covenant put forth by the Richards didn't just target the intelligence. Leading readers toward that *bright-shining horizon* suggested covert soul work.

The most famous Richard was a Raymond, of course, depicting a character with sight helping a blind man feel what a cathedral looks like, the two of them like writer and reader exploring the dimensions of a miniature representation in someone's living room of something massive out there in the world. Instead of telling you, the story, like the character with sight, shows you, the blind man, the reader, and yet presented in a straightforward way by these Richards, there's no sense of condescension, comparing a reader to someone without sight or envisioning them as an aging couple on a ranch listening to homemade recordings of stories as the sun sets, a couple stranded on their island, surrounded by a churning ocean of earth. It's not condescending because Richards respect the reader's blindness, they respect the simplicity of the couple out west, they hold up the readers whose hearts they hunt as ideal quarry, and other readers who aren't blind or aren't couples out west listening to recordings of stories can lose their oh so educated pretentiousness for a second and stoop to the level of the blind reader, can come off it and sit and listen beside the couple out west. Surely the most sophisticated readers in the most sophisticated corners of the most sophisticated cities have the capacity as readers and fellow human beings to follow these stories, fall under their sway. What good is sophistication if it can't appreciate a simple story told well about something good in a world with a tendency to reveal itself as neutral and therefore *cruel*, a world that requires its occupants to rebuild it anew each day and breathe it to life and fill out its height, length, depth, and the fourth dimension of time, the crucial dimension for stories, the string that binds memory to reality, that ties past, present, and future until one's map of histories and hopes resembles blueprints for a cathedral intended to rise piece by piece on pace with one's progress through life, until over time a cathedral can be seen at all times existing in one's imagination, an inch or two behind one's eyes, always there, a sacred place constructed of associated experience, a safe place, the palace of the kingdom of the heaven within.

Something along these lines at most minimalist Richard stories suggest their fiction can do, like a magic trick, like the Japanese paper flower that rises out of a bowl of water as described by Proust toward the beginning of *Swann's Way*, which also exhaustively describes the cathedral in Combray early on, but looking over at England now next to Snare as he settles in and orders a relatively high ABV India Pale Ale and digs in for the first sips of what should be a promising session, it's clear this idea of a suggested house of nondenominational worship inside oneself he would deem a little much. He's the sort of writer who focuses on the heart, maybe a bit of the guts when the heart hurts, the sort of writer who avoids ideas, who doesn't think they have a place in fiction, something I deny and cite all the canonical biggies as evidence in the defense of ideas.

Ideas don't need to be daggers. Ideas can create a space the way the walls of a cathedral and the roof create a space, something Jonathan David Grooms respects in his fiction, something I would argue that makes him who he is, advances his reputation, the ideas part of what he does, not all that he does but part of what he does, something so few writers now seem to do.

X.

England's talking about how, knowing that tonight he'd be here and tomorrow he'd be incapacitated, he spent the day in his apartment editing his latest novel manuscript as though it just needs shaping, tightening, believing revision will set him free into the life of a writer with a published book, so when other writers think of John England they think of the author of *How the Living Returned to Life*, author of *Austerity Rock*, author of *The Labor Day Parade*, author of *How We Talk About Hope*. Those are just guesses at the likely title of his new novel. I'd read his last manuscript and some stories before that but since my response to his last manuscript I've been cut off from reading his writing, either because he doesn't want me to see it or because he doesn't want me to tell him what I think about it, the way I told him what I thought about his last novel manuscript, whatever it was called. That was one of my critiques, the first thing I balked at. Circled the title, noted a need for something more memorable.

Some titles are so difficult to remember, you satirize them, sodomize them by approximation, something like *And Then We Leave*, or *And So Now We Go*, the words *Go* or *Leave* were definitely in the title. *Those Who Leave And Those Who Never Go* sounds more like it but not quite right, although it actually sounds like what his title was going for, something classic like *And Then There Were None*, but not memorable like that, even if he may have remembered it fine, the title something like *Those Who Leave Never Go Far*. Or *We Leave So Others May Stay*?

I should interrupt and ask apropos of nothing what was the title of your last manuscript, the one I read and wrote all over, the one I took a week to precisely line edit and type eleven pages of single-spaced notes about characterization, structure, theme, setting, description, scene, as a sort of volunteer work. But also of course I realize it's possible I was applying to some abstract idea of the Iowa Writers' Workshop, trying to exceed in effort and excellence anything he might expect to receive from MFA-addled writers who read his manuscript. To an extent I admit that when I read England's last manuscript it wasn't so much about helping a writing career that depends on the success of his project. I cared more about receiving validation for the obsessive-compulsive clarity of my response to his manuscript, cleaning lax lines, suggesting wholesale structural revision to elevate what seemed like a linear exercise in narrative accessibility into something that suggested classic novels that covered the same terrain but did so in ways that evoked a sense of wilderness. I tried to suggest that his project would benefit from the erection of *Faulknerian thickets* throughout the prairies and plains he'd described. His linear structure felt less like step-by-step ascension than meaningless progress across a dusty void, OK if about Okies fleeing the Dustbowl but it was about growing up in the Pacific Northwest in a town between Seattle and Portland, a town more or less exactly how he'd described his hometown. Meaningless progress across dusty void was more about the future the kid felt having been raised among evergreens and fog and winding roads with vistas on clear days of mountains and volcanoes and the sense the flora was prehistoric, that they lived in an area existing before history, before the continent was settled even by ancients coming in from Alaska along the coast from the north. There was this eternal present England lived in as a child, radiant green contrasted with fog that broke at most for a string of days when verdant undergrowth gave way to the Technicolor brilliance of full sun, cottony pulls of cloud at play in deep blue skies, the atmosphere backed by an infinite expanse of dark matter.

This is what I remember from the manuscript, not the title or the narrator's name or anything much that occurs. It's a coming-of-age novel wherein the narrator leaves (per the misremembered title) for college on the East Coast and returns after his first year and runs around with old friends who'd stayed, like *Less Than Zero* but without a classic, memorable title, and without a memorable narrator, and without coyotes or snuff films or driving around and savoring youthful nihilism nurtured by environment and privileged natures. Instead it's scenes set in woods, hiking to streams and rocks and waterfalls, fishing, old-fashioned weed smoke, childhood retreats and desires to escape the preserve they'd created, what they'd once been so proud of. There's a showdown in the woods, a shotgun makes an appearance, and there's a surprisingly violent scene involving a banana slug. From what I remember it ends with everything up in the air, unresolved. It's all rendered in a clear, clipped style, short bursts of dialogue interspersed with gesture and summary of talk and action, much of the important stuff unspoken and suggested by the unimportant stuff they talk about.

England describes his day of revision on his new novel manuscript, the moves he made, hours spent printing his manuscript and laying the pages around his apartment. The more I think about his last manuscript, the more I like it, but maybe that has less to do with what he wrote than with my comments, the book I thought his book could become if he revised it and erected *Faulknerian thickets*.

England across the booth offering intricate machinations of a day on his laptop, strapped to his seat like out on a deep-sea fishing boat. That's what he says it's like, in a rocking chair with his laptop, hauling in the catch of the manuscript he's been working on for more than two years, the novel manuscript he's reeling in via dedicated revision. Every cut, every move, every addition brings him closer to success defined as a published book to associate with his name.

I imagine if he were to publish a book he would burst into light. He would be complete as a human being, without regrets, existing beyond desire of any sort. He would stroke his published book and sleep with it and the book would be who he was and vice versa and all the years spent writing it and not writing it and writing other stuff that was necessary to write before he could write his published book he would consider time well spent. The published book would val-idate England to himself and friends and parents and employers, some of which is true and some of which isn't, since it'd help him with employers but not so much with parents or friends or himself since of course once the book published the next question would be how did it sell, how was it received, *what next?*

Once you've written a book that disappears after publication sans notable sales or reviews, are you better off back where you'd been a year ago working with the desire to be published, thinking that the harder you worked the better your chances of publication, not thinking about critical success or sales or the likelihood of ever publishing future work? And so maybe it would be best if once the book were published but before anyone really has the chance to *not* buy it or any reviewers have the chance to *not* review it or review it poorly that England there and then *bursts into light*, there and then be-fore the enthusiasm for achieving the goal of publication wears off he *bursts into light* before anxiety about his career's next stage kicks in and he starts worrying about writing another novel when all that effort led to nothing more than a half-hearted review on a random blog or two.

At least for now he's saying he figured he'd come have some beers. Same as usual, with Snare and Roebling and Oates and Guardian and whoever else, but this time with the great Jonathan David Grooms.

England's heard good things, likes his writing and teaches a story written when Grooms was in college. He loves teaching it to kids in college because it's so much better than anything they write but not unlike what they write, he says.

England has downed his first pint in record time, or maybe time has passed and I haven't noticed since his voice hypnotizes. I have to force myself to focus or else fall into a dream. Snare interjects, Snare spurs him on, but I might as well not exist. It's not the worst place to be, although it'd be better if I had a view of the room, only able to see to my left down the bar and the line of bar stools.

What a way to spend time, sitting there as I sat there so often easing churning thoughts before I'd met my wife, the way England churns on publication, thoughts of publication like a chew toy. It would be great if his book were published so he could work on something new, think about something else, have the confidence of a published book behind him and use it to leap into a new mode of writing, more confident about what he can do. He's always trying to validate himself, the way I tried to validate myself by writing that long single-spaced response to his manuscript, thereby ensuring that no one would ever ask me to read one of their manuscripts again because no one wants anyone to line edit and respond with eleven single-spaced pages of notes about how a manuscript the writer considers done could be improved, the suggestion that instead of being done the work has only just begun.

I gave him that sort of input because he'd graduated from the so-called *Workshop* and I wanted to prove that I knew my stuff, prove that I had read more than he had and had more fluent thoughts about fiction based on reading and experience and writing, and that just because I didn't have a diploma from the University of Iowa it didn't mean that I wasn't a serious writer who in fact, in part because I hadn't gone to the so-called *Workshop*, harbored unique responses to manuscripts based on all the books I'd read that he and his fellow

Workshop friends hadn't read, beyond *Jesus' Son* or the Cheever stories or Breece DJ'Pancake or James Salter or any of the other short fiction writers they all seemed to revere.

They seemed to have no idea that fiction written in countries other than the United States and United Kingdom was almost always better than books written in English. Translated literature they believed couldn't help "the project" of their fiction, of their essentially derivative attempts to write American literary fiction that seemed in tone and theme like iterations of American literary fiction recently published and received with enthusiasm. The conversation they were having was with the American literary fiction industry, which wanted to see a certain sort of American literary fiction. As a writer of American literary fiction it was an honest goal to provide publishers and editors and agents and reviewers and booksellers what they wanted, although it was clear that readers weren't sure what they wanted. They wanted something good, something different but not too different, something easy to read but not too easy to read, something like the writing offered by Jonathan David Grooms, who as I order my third hefeweizen I'm not sure I admire or despise.

The more I think about Grooms, the more I admire him, but earlier in the day while arranging books in associative order on the new shelves at home, re-establishing the Throop Roebling Memorial Library of Canonical Excellence, it didn't seem like Jonathan David Grooms amounted to much, whereas next to Snare and England and me he's clearly a demigod. Listening to England and Snare talk about what they're working on, which agents have responded, which novels and story collections they're reading, each basking in their summer vacations from teaching composition and fiction, as I take the first sips of a third beautiful *Weihenstephaner Hefeweizen* I'm beginning to long for Jonathan David Grooms's arrival. Maybe he'll recognize a special quality once he settles down and figures out a way to sit next to me or follow me when I slip out to bum a smoke?

He'll bum one too and hardly take a drag as we discuss Molly Bloom and the idea of the masterpiece more than the masterpiece itself, the ridiculousness of celebrating a book more than a hundred years after it supposedly takes place. We'll gesture toward the smoke and ashes and cracked sidewalk and say this will all be around longer than anything anyone writes, even what Joyce wrote. We'll tip our hats to the temporary existence of literate culture on the planet, acknowledge that smoke and ash and concrete will outlast words on pages. He'll mention Faulkner's Nobel speech, how human beings will do more than endure, and we'll tip our hats in the direction of prevailing against the forces of ash and smoke and concrete. Human beings with their language, human beings with weird rare offspring natured and nurtured to give a shit about lit, about the charged and concentrated arrangement of experience real and imagined represented in the charged and concentrated arrangement of text, a charged and concentrated existence at one with our quivering ribbons of breath.

Jonathan David Grooms and Throop Roebling sometime in the next hours will be allied in the struggle against complacency, apathy, fear, inelegant simplicity, straight-up stupidity, aesthetic conformity, selfish prolixity, blunted garrulousness, on and on, supported by the spines amassed on our bookshelves, soldiers of lore rising to reinforce the columns of bone that connect our brains and bodies and gird our resolve as we recommit to battle the Axis of Idiocy, benighted by mutual recognition of something like what once may have been called the Holy Spirit, a composite of talent, practice, experience, education, intuition, restlessness, discipline, precision, respect for indeterminacy, lack of rigidity, an instinct to argue in surfeit.

Jonathan David Grooms and Throop Roebling smoking outside the bar, a little lit, elevating air held within toward skyscrapers a 25-minute walk to the northwest, like Old World castles on a hill, too obvious an enemy, but then Snare brings me back to the booth, the tabletop, the pints, my golden chalice topped with foam. Snare snaps me back to the booth with a sudden increase in intensity, as though England uttering the name "Driscoll" were a spark that turns the ever-agitated aura around Snare into open flame.

XI.

Snare slams the table with an open hand. His ring adds a metallic crack to the slap. He shouts *Driscoll*, as though someone named Driscoll who just entered had perpetrated a great injustice against Snare and his family and also maybe did something awful to Snare's dog.

Snare and England often discussed fellow students from their creative writing graduate program but all the names ran together for me. Even those they brought up more than once, all were faceless surnames that for Snare and England conjured stills and snippets of movement and language, a glow or pallor animated by their memories. But the names were just names to me, a wash, like when I looked at Oates's most recent novel manuscript and noted he suffered from Disembodied Proper Noun Syndrome.

Characters need flesh and breath and gestures, they need *to stand and cast a shadow*, as Faulkner said, or as someone had said about Faulkner's characters, but when talking about assorted friends and foes from grad school I only register cursory description, as though Snare and England are unaware that when they talk I only see cartoon renditions of some gentleman empress draped in boas knocking back uppers and downers and every-which-wayers, not calling it a night until he's propositioned every man at the after party. Stray instances presented in the continual past. Once this guy had some pills out in the open in his kitchen after he brought the party back to his place once the bar closed and maybe around four in the morning for half an hour he became jelly-limbed and omni-affectionate and solicitous of affection in return, indiscriminate to the point of attempting to smooch the uneven cheeks of Snare. The pill-popper for half an hour exceeded expectations of behavior, so Snare forever immortalized him at his most unrestrained, memorable, atypical moment, and so instead of having any real sense of a human being I envisioned a cartoon. Animation of an uncharacteristic instance was all I had to work with, triaging the description as they spoke, not interrupting, imagining the guy the next day hungover, regretful, showering memories off him of Snare pushing him away, saying he's flattered but that's really not his jawn whereas only five years earlier in high school Snare would have flipped on the guy, Snare proud of his maturity and improved worldview, the exaggerated description a trophy brought back from graduate school. Snare, *even Snare*, had a friend who was a sexually aggressive pill-popping gay guy, imprecise reality adding another dimension to Snare, the exaggerated description flung as far as Snare could fling it so the spike off Snare's axis created an appearance of open-mindedness and tolerance. Snare stole the guy's identity via misrepresentation and did so to overcompensate for what had been unfortunate immature episodes in his own history. He flung the misrepresentation as far as it could fly and, like an over-sized flying disc in the form of a wide open circle of flexible rubber, the characterization flew much farther than anything with the heft and complexity of reality, mostly because such stories weren't about grad school or the people who populated it but about what set Snare apart from everyone he'd grown up with and his family, validated the sense Snare had always had that he was in fact *special*, the way even the most humble at times think they're special and their special qualities will one day be recognized, even if over time these qualities are only understood and validated by furry non-verbal dependents. Snare won't have kids but he'll have furry non-verbal dependents who will validate him in the future.

I always forget how important this was to them, how big a deal the so-called *Workshop* was to Snare and England in a way it hadn't been for Oates and Gibson, who were about ten years older and had traveled and moved around and worked before they went there. Two years at the so-called *Workshop* was just another chapter for them, not the climax, but there was something about the way Snare says this one particular disembodied proper noun, Driscoll, that seems charged with real undisguised unfiltered anger, something deep and uncontrollable, like Snare's core were still filled with something molten, volatile. When this fire escapes from the largest hole in Snare's face I have a sense he can be *a great writer*, not just a good one. He's blessed with a core of fire, an essential gutful of anger. If he manages to release it through his fingertips before it consumes him or before he squelches it with drink and domesticity and obsessive-compulsive commentary on the constantly refreshing timelines of sports results and related stories, if he somehow learns to release that rage a bit at a time into text, he'll be in great shape.

The way Snare yells *Driscoll* resembles a young athlete revealing natural talent that can be nurtured and become something special at the highest level of competition, a revelation of his natural resource, talent born not so much of exposure to literature and education and individuated perception but simply *a gutful of fire* that wasn't something anyone set out to learn, gas in Snare's tank if he's able to use it without imploding or exploding or somehow destroying himself if he mismanages its volatility.

Driscoll, Snare shouts, and he shouts it a few more times, at first I think unconscious of the fact that he's shouted, and then aware, and then embarrassed but not as much as it angers him, this idea of Driscoll, whatever this particular disembodied proper noun means to him, mixed with the first few beers and the volatile molten substance in his gut combined to combust, like from waist to neck he bursts into flames, with his embarrassed head doing what it can to calm himself.

He finishes his pint, half in one go, and calls for another. Our friendly energetic server hurries off like it's a medical emergency, as though without application of a fresh pint he'll foul the evening for everyone. Even over the jukebox, louder in the bar area than where we sit, heads turn to see what that guy's yelling about, some guy without tattoos sitting next to some guy in a polo shirt and shiny bald head, across from some nondescript dude sitting in the wooden Viking booth beneath the chalkboard listing all the fancy pints available tonight.

Our presence in the wooden Viking booth beneath the chalkboard had not seemed registered by anyone other than our attentive and friendly server, but once Snare revealed his native resource, we were on the map of the world enclosed within this quasi-Transylvanian purveyor of fine ales, lagers, porters, stouts, sours, kölsches. It is, after all, a Saturday evening in the middle of June, the true start of summer. Those not already spending the night or weekend at the beach or otherwise exploring the world now that the weather is perfect are staying in town, saving money on gas and lodging and requisite consumption of rest-stop food. Otherwise, for super-pregnant wife and me, the world shuts down as we prepare to experience it through the eyes of our child.

Driscoll mutters Snare, simmering, blinded by shaking head.

I say so who's this Driscoll?

I picture our child all grown up, someone we're proud of, roundly hated by the likes of some future Snare. I take the side of this Driscoll, defend this Driscoll like my son. It's shaping up into that sort of night, contrarian tendencies stirred by golden chalices of ancient recipe wheat beer. It may not be remembered for the one hundred and eighth anniversary of Bloomsday or eventual appearance of Jonathan David Grooms, but one day I'll remember it as the

Driscoll Affair. Snare at this point has only shouted the name a few times and muttered it a few more but I'm already tossing it into the deep space of time, twelve years ahead when these shouts and mutters have lost contact with their origins and evolved into mythology.

Classmate from Iowa, says England. Harvard grad, rich kid from around Boston, a little young, not just in age. Her fiction situated itself in her early teens, always narrated from the same perspective, the same smart, informed, clueless kid with nose pressed against the window separating her cloistered existence from the real world. You know the sort of stories about rich important families at rich important weddings and rich important golf courses, doorman buildings in New York, her stuff was set there, doorman buildings that seemed to exist more in Cheever stories than in the real world. No one other than the help seemed to work, no one seemed to have jobs except the doormen. So whenever she tried to write about someone in their twenties Kev attacked her for having no clue what it's like to be twenty-something in a city with a job you hate, not that Kev had much experience with that at the time, other than a summer job through high school and college making hoagies at some deli on Cheltenham Avenue, but he hated her with such passion that you could tell he saw something in her he hated in himself. In a way they were soulmates separated by a couple hundred miles and several hundred thousand annual dollars in parental salaries. Culturally they were different species but in every other way they were the same. Like our friend Snare here, England says, she had a temper that'd be revealed when she workshopped Snare's stories of course but even when she workshopped my stories. I always found her critiques humorous since they were venomous, ad hominem almost, articulate takedowns of me or Snare or others she didn't care for. She critiqued not only our manuscripts but also our characters. She didn't care about the stories we put up. She was more interested in critiquing what she saw as faults in our characters that manifested in our writing, not that she said it that way but you could tell she was trying to let us know she saw through us and wanted to help us by taking apart everything we stood for, England says, not that we stood for much, which was her primary complaint, not that she or her fiction stood for anything either. So I think the problem was that she hated what she saw of herself in me and Snare, and the feeling was mutual, mostly, but there was also something normal about her stuff I liked. It was conventional in a classic way, and I admire good old-fashioned honest normality more than convoluted hyperbolic skewed quasi-autobiographical indulgence with dialogue presented in long run-on sentences sans quotation marks, for example. But generally we didn't know enough at the time to steer clear of someone like Driscoll and Workshop social life since we only had our crappy apartments and the bars, we were on one another too much, so Driscoll by the first semester of the second year was Kev's mortal enemy, England says.

I tip my scepter of glowing golden wheat beer at Snare and suggest he explain himself.

Snare says oh it's just, it's just *she makes me so mad*, and then he laughs, recognizing he sounds ridiculous, and then he says he'd forgotten her more or less until five or six years after graduation she had a thing in *Glimmer Train* and another in *A Public Space* and then she may have had another story somewhere good, like the *Indiana Review* or *Missouri Review* or *New England Review*, one of those academic reviews with a stream and a windmill on the cover, but then she disappeared, as far as I knew, Snare says, and I rarely thought of her, until I saw that the same agent who nearly took my last novel but strung me along for five months before saying she didn't think she could sell it wound up selling Sarah Driscoll's first novel for six figures. She probably already had six figures in her checking account without even working, an apartment in New York, in Chelsea, and she sells her book about a preppie funeral set along the New England coast, Rhode

Island or somewhere, and it's from a precocious teenage girl's perspective. The cover is mostly white with the title in big letters and her name even larger, like they're pushing her debut, making her name visible. Of everyone we were at Iowa with for Driscoll to be the first to hit one out like this . . . I mean Nam Le had a pretty big story collection, won every award in Australia, I'm legitimately happy for him, I'd prefer if he were happy for me but maybe that time will come, for now I'm happy for him, he returns my emails, calls me "mate," no one else calls me "mate," but Sarah Driscoll, someone says *Kev Snare* and a second later she clears her throat and hacks up something nasty and expels it as fast as possible as far away as she can. I think what it was was that Driscoll was passionately in love with me, hadn't ever met someone who only ever dressed in sweatshirts covered in the logo of an NFL team. She'd never met someone who hadn't gone to an Ivy who didn't seem all that impressed with her, found her mousy and flawed instead of cute and charismatic. How can anyone be in love with someone like a plane of glass floating out in the middle of an empty lot with rocks all around and no one in sight. All you want to do is *shatter it*, it'd be so easy, so fragile, almost like she wants someone to come along and smash it, and I think she thought I was that person because I didn't fall for cute and charismatic. She thought I was maybe the one to shatter her so she could become something new. I doubt she thought that on a conscious level, just that I can't think of why else she sent such animosity my way. I can quote what she said about me, every time I put up a story in Charlie D'Ambrosio's workshop, every time I put up a story I did so rubbing my hands to see what Driscoll would say in her letter, how it'd differ from what she'd said in class. What she said in class would be a little performance letting D'Ambrosio and everyone know how well she could apply subtleties of point of view or parrot something Frank or Marilynne had said, something about how *the story has no memory of itself*, something socially acceptable like that, but then the letter, especially if she'd been tame in the workshop itself, the letter would rip me. Such a great talent for abusive writing. It's like she thought I could take it and so she'd unleash hostility and I'd deflect it or at least not return it to an equal degree, not because I was a softie but maybe she thought I was a poor kid from Northeast Philadelphia and I wouldn't attack a cute and charismatic girl from Harvard who happened to be batshit nutso. The things she said to me, the phrasing, the takedowns of man and manuscript . . . I've heard people call Iowa *competitive* but I never thought that was right, I always thought the word *competitive* must have been used in terms of admissions, like it's one of the most *competitive* programs to get into, I've heard it's harder to get into than Harvard Law, but that doesn't mean students are *competitive* once there, once there I didn't sense *competition* at all, it wasn't *competitive*, although maybe comments were sometimes *competitive* in that students seemed to *compete* to write the most helpful, insightful, awesome notes on your stuff. One older student in particular wrote six single-spaced pages about my first story, which he copyedited, I mean precise line edits with legible notes in the margins, and he also ordered a used book for me to read that related in his mind to my story, something by an Austrian dude with longish hair and glasses who'd written a weird little book about a killer and a penalty kick and an anxious goalie. I didn't read the book but I read his notes dozens of times. They weren't *competitive*. If there'd been a *competition* for the most helpful, precise, clear comments they obliterated the competition with cooperative kindness, lack of professional or artistic competition. Instead of seeming *competitive* it was communal and supportive but not sentimental and touchy-feely. It wasn't necessarily nurturing but it wasn't *competitive*, or it was competitive only in that some students asserted themselves as authorities, competed for an authoritarian role. You get the point, most comments were helpful and thorough, more interesting than whatever story I submitted, more artful, or at least they said some good things, some critical things, never trying to hurt the writer's feelings, but then whenever I received comments I'd make a little stack and put her sheet at the end. Only with Driscoll did I suspect she was trying to obliterate my confidence, completely undermine me, turn me into a self-conscious mess next time I sat down to write. It was almost like she wanted to force me to stop going to workshop so she could reign over everyone with cuteness and charisma, so she could put up stories in which no one needed to work, stories about people in the top 10% of the top 1%, but I don't think she tried to obliterate me because she was wealthy and wrote about wealthy people and I grew up poor and wrote about poor people. I think she had a crush on me and hated herself for it and didn't even recognize it herself, whereas while everyone was praising her stories for being like Cheever's, I ripped them for being unrealistic, for getting basic things about humanity wrong, for imitating Cheever, too. I thought they were weak teenage renditions of classic Cheever stories, "Goodbye My Brother" over and over from the point of view of an adolescent girl. Decaying old house on the New England coast, older preppie types drinking way too much, adolescent girl taking it all in, loving it, hating it, a swim in the ocean always so spiritually refreshing et cetera. This older well-read opinionated student at the Workshop read one of her stories and said she should get a menial job in New York or Boston and live in a shared apartment for three years and write and read and have *two nervous breakdowns* before she wrote fiction again. He was ten years older than us at the time and like a literary physician after reading one story he prescribed subsistence living, lots of reading and writing, and two nervous breakdowns, not just one nervous breakdown, but two nervous breakdowns. Who knows what sort of life she's led since Iowa, I haven't kept in touch, but whenever I think of her I picture her in the throes of her *second nervous breakdown*, unable to do anything other than make everyone around her miserable as life beyond the structure of school helps her shed her skin. She had always been in elite schools from some fancy grade school to some fancy prep school and then to Harvard, directly to Iowa, directly to Chelsea, where what she'd been working on at Iowa, a novel, must have been rejected by everyone. Which sent her into a state liable to collapse and then she did collapse. Everything that animated her presence across the Workshop table from me, I imagined her emptied of wrath, spite, condescension, everything that made her the girl I knew. I saw her like an empty pillow case, and I admit I sometimes fantasized about her in that broken-down state. I love my wife and all but I sometimes fantasized about her deflated and defeated at the kitchen table of her Chelsea apartment, trying to drink but failing to get much into her system through all her pathetic sobs.

England instructs me that the key bit our friend Kev here has failed to relay is that Sarah Driscoll at the party after the Workshop prom dance at the end of their last semester pulled Kev behind a shed behind whoever's house the after-party was held at and proceeded to devour his face. At the time Kev described it in terms of a snake unhooking its jaw to swallow its prey. Driscoll opened her mouth as wide as she could to swallow Kev from head to foot. That's the way he described it to me at least, England says.

Snare says thing is, it was hot, even if she had no idea how to kiss, was so drunk she was trying to mouth my face and head, hair and all. It was this crazy release of tension, everything made sense after it. Driscoll was one of those girls who hated boys she liked, treated them like crap so they'd treat her nice. It was a primal, uneducated, uncivilized thing for such an educated, civilized girl. She more or less tried to kill me in workshops because she recognized there was something about me she'd fallen for, I guess, but *hey* what's not to love? Snare pats his chest and shrugs, his complexion so chalk-like his mouth seems drawn in burgundy lipstick.

I can't imagine this cute fancy young woman falling for Snare. Maybe she couldn't imagine the attraction either so she rebelled? I'd never heard of her but the next time I look at *The New Yorker* or *The New York Times Book Review* I'm sure I'll see something by or about her. It always works like that.

The literary world is no larger than the country of Monaco and everyone's rebelling against their attraction or repulsion to someone within it, something about it, attracted or repulsed by every particular element, but it seems to me the trick involves magnifying and announcing attractions and minimizing or at least *restraining* repulsions. Anyone can magnify and announce true attraction but the trick is to magnify and announce minor attraction without undermining integrity.

The trick is to take natural apathy or even antipathy and apply supremely generous perception to it, massage it, roll it between fingers with extreme tenderness like a baby bird with a hammering startled heart until you find the good in this someone or something you might otherwise have no feelings for or that might even repulse you.

The trick is to turn what otherwise may have been natural apathetic or *anti*pathetic feelings and thanks to concentration, empathy, mindfulness, all those good words, extract from the apathy and even *anti*pathy the startled hammering bird heart at the core of someone or something you actually honestly think is total trash or, to a lesser degree, simply dull or insipid, possibly even satanically so. Instead of dwelling on satanic mediocrity the trick is to seek out and nurture seeds of excellence. The trick is not wearing your heart on your sleeve but envisioning the heart of someone or something hammering like crazy, truly freaking out, and if encouraging generous helpful affirming words don't spill from your lips the hammering will slow and stop and you'll look at your sleeve a little up the arm from where you might wear a watch and there you'll see the stopped heart of something in need of help.

The trick is to overcome immediate negative impressions to reveal *the fragile hammering bird heart* of novels considered contemporary masterpieces. The trick when it comes to novels deemed contemporary masterpieces is not to throw them across the room when reading blurbs and advanced praise trying to convince someone to part with cash. The trick is to treat the hyped commercially and critically successful contemporary masterpiece as something fragile and perishable as yourself, since hyping is a disservice to a novel and anyone's appreciation of it, a disservice to a reader willing to see something that otherwise doesn't exist, that relates to the real world but isn't the real world, that takes the real world and sharpens it, organizes it, charges it, warps it, so the experience seems intense to someone otherwise only sitting wherever they prefer to sit and read, a world that seems real and makes the world itself seem even more real, more urgent, less familiar, more important than it did before the book was opened.

The trick is not to indulge in worst actions, such as criticizing something you can try to love and support, and that's a trick I've never cared for, England has never cared for, and Snare hasn't cared for either.

What's great about drinking excessive beer in this massive quasi Transylvanian booth is that it's perfect for eating out the hearts of everything. Over time, we become ravenous and cannibalistic, insatiable when it comes to a desire to devour the flesh of everything and everyone, wanting to take it into us, chew it up, expel it with force into the least lovely bathroom in town, even on a busy Saturday night in mid-June. Now that Snare has presented his case against Sarah Driscoll I sense canines growing in expectation of reviewing her prose, savoring an immediate negative impression as I snap the hardback shut and return it to a tall stack of first editions on a table upfront at a major national chain bookseller featuring titles from major New York publishers, minor subsidiaries of massive international conglomerates based in Western Europe and owned by invisible holding companies in East Asia with only a handful of executive officers with any connection to the true owners who might not even know what every entity of the conglomerate produces, only aware of their contribution in profit or debt to the overall holding company, the offices of which are paperless, the windows floor to ceiling, the employees limited to assistants who field requests for conference calls with the holding company's limited group of persons of power, each as airy and light and impressive as their high-rise offices, who analyze elegant presentations and whisper determinations and suggested decisions, all actions and operations quantifiable. So methodical and elegant, executive officer actions could be replaced by applications installed on slim laptops to determine the fate of the massive international entertainment conglomerate, a small division of which is the publishing segment, an even smaller division of which is the so-called prestige division that produces literary fiction intended to serve as brand ambassador for the overall publisher and international conglomerate, if not the holding company solely operating on a quantifiable level unrelated to abstractions such as prestige. A stable of writers who have won Pulitzers and National Book Awards is meaningless to the occupants of the office around which the sun orbits like a silent partner, its presence filling the windows with majesty and grandeur, a form as perfect and as inarguable as a spreadsheet column terminating in a show of profit, infused by so much sunlight, well beyond prestige, another word for dusty respectable loss, the asphyxiated neck of a minor division of a publishing division of a major international entertainment conglomerate dressed up with a ridiculous bow-tie. The minor literary publishing unit disguises loss with the bow-tie of prestige, something the larger publishing division touts more than the major international entertainment conglomerate whenever the minor literary unit fails to produce blockbusters involving wizards, vampires, or sadomasochists.

Whenever the minor literary unit strikes it rich they tout their numbers, but when no wizards, vampires, or sadomasochists come to the rescue, they parade the prize-winners, something for which no column of cells exists on spreadsheets appearing on monitors the size and thickness of world maps on chrome-magnesium desks reflecting the sun through windows of an office atop a skyscraper in a forest of skyscrapers, each constructed to sway with grace whenever the Earth's crust tries to topple the forest's relationship with the sun, illuminating ultra-thin screens synched to the thoughts of executive officers in command, each nearly weightless, bodies wafted by thoughts. Whenever wizards, vampires, or sadomasochists come to the rescue of the minor literary unit, it's noted in a sub-cell of a column of a spreadsheet pertaining to North American publishing units within larger international publishing divisions but more often than not the number is only one on a spreadsheet in flux per quarter, conforming to expectations of constant change, coming together with everything else to show slow and steady growth at a sustainable rate.

XII.

It's a special occasion, the one hundred and eighth anniversary of Bloomsday, but still there's some concern about the price of the fancy beers, since each costs five or six dollars, the cheapest four dollars per pint or three dollars in a bottle. Achieving and maintaining a semi-inebriated state for hours could cost more than fifty dollars, more if tempted by appetizers, the bill growing in increments of four, five, six dollars with every glass that arrives. Only three participants so far, Oates and Gibson and Guardian still to come, maybe others, not to mention Jonathan David Grooms, who at the end of the evening if we're lucky will put everything on a credit card provided by the minor literary unit of the major publishing division within the massive international entertainment conglomerate owned by a holding company on the other side of the planet that deals in so much more than the expense account of a minor literary unit in New York.

I wonder if we can write this off, I say, since it's a writing-related expense? I wonder if we can write it off as a business expense?

I've never bothered to keep track of writing-related expenses because I've never declared income from writing work, but if I ever sold something I wonder if I could declare all books purchased over the past year as business expenses? I am the owner of a small business focused on the provision of literary fiction for readers with too much time on their hands, a masochistic bent, a heroic side, a screw loose. I am such a small business I can't even declare myself a small business and therefore can't expense books but what about time walking and reading? If I were truly a small business I would expense time writing, reading, and walking while reading, not to mention sneakers and shorts. Even my socks would be a business expense. Inner thigh anti-chafe moisturizer too. Pockets stuffed with receipts because I am a small business owner whose business is literary fiction production. A tiny smokestack rises like an antenna from the spot where spine meets brain, hard at work, emitting the byproducts of literary fiction production into the atmosphere, toxic stuff that imagination, intuition, talent, and skill burn off when applied to the raw material of memory and reality.

Snare says *expense* doesn't always refer to taxes, the whole night will be an expense.

He's paying for remembering Sarah Driscoll as his first beers take effect.

Expense for Snare seems to mean *cost*, a noun, not a verb.

Snare says don't you feel like we're sitting ducks, waiting like this?

A light in England's eye is lit by the idea that the expanse of wood at which we sit is not the table element of an oversized wooden booth but a pool of water in rural Pennsylvania: we're enjoying ourselves, waiting for friends to arrive, just a few waterfowl, fine feathered friends, when lo and behold there comes a cacophonous blast.

I see England dreaming about this, memory and imagination activating the scene across his forehead, wrinkling it out, and so it's expected when he looks around and says something about how a man and his new son-in-law on a hunting trip just walked into the bar, a man and his son-in-law on a hunting trip, the stuff of classic male-bonding, the younger guy married the older guy's only daughter after knowing her less than a year, the older guy is conservative, England says, voted LBJ, Nixon, Ford, Reagan, Reagan, Bush, Bush, Dole, Bush, Bush, McCain, and has already cast a vote in his mind for Romney.

England hijacks whatever Snare may want to say about sitting ducks so Snare now seems agitated and drinks his drink a little faster but then realizes there's nothing he can do but sit it out and wait for England to improvise this scene in which father and son-in-law take positions in the barroom using the fleshier clientele as blinds, intending to down us in such a way that suggests a subtle symbolic parallel about the time-honored transference of responsibility and doing so through the ecstatic percussive expression of a shotgun blast.

England's version focuses on conflict in the son-in-law's heart about whether he should be true to his jokey self, debating whether being true to his jokey inappropriate self is more important than performing his role in the manly hunting ritual. Stakes are high. The relationship could blow up with daughter if son/husband agitates father/father-in-law but also son/husband could be blown up with a close-range shotgun blast to the head or heart, guts or nuts.

We look toward the barroom as England talks this hunting duo into life, united to bag their quarry, floating exposed on an expanse of tabletop. The two fire at once, a bond that scrubs the "in-law" aspects from their relationship. They've attempted to destroy three birds floating at peace. The ritual completed. And then right after England says the imaginary father/son duo fired their rifles I feel a sharp pain in the shoulder facing these nonexistent hunters. Snare and England seem fine but my shoulder feels like it's been punched.

I'd been lifting weights recently so I'd be able to walk around holding a kid without a problem. My shoulder had felt sore while walking and reading along the river loop. For the most part I had held the book in my right hand or held it lower than I normally do with my left. There was a presence there I hadn't felt before, a subtle charley horse, but now it's a throb. I've only had a few beers, not counting those two quick glasses of wine before I left, but I haven't eaten anything, so maybe I'm dehydrated. I raise my right hand and flag down the server and ask for two pints of water. She hurries off and returns and I thank her and down both pints.

Snare says so as they walk out the door, neither having hit shit, son puts muzzle to back of father's skull and splatters brains all over the door, which opens, and then the headless body, its heart beating a few last furious times, drops at the feet of patrons newly arrived to join us at the booth in the back.

Snare avenged England's hijacking of Snare's comment about feeling like sitting ducks by escalating the conflict of England's story to full-on homicidal psychopathic horror, something surprising yet not at all inevitable, an example of authorial heavy-handedness, England argues:

You can't just take these guys who took shots at us and missed and then headed home, realizing they didn't want to kill anything because now there's this bond between them, they didn't want to sacrifice important parts of a duck family when they'd just deepened the bond so important to their own family, you can't just have the son who at most wanted to be himself and say some off-color things here and there, you can't just say the son will escalate things from figuratively shooting himself in the foot to literally shooting the father in the back of the head. It's implausible and leaves the reader thinking that nothing makes sense in the world. We're all endangered by homicidal forces animating our loved ones. Never turn your back. That's the lingering impression? Never trust anyone, especially if they hold a firearm.

Snare argues that the story doesn't make sense. Why would they take one shot each, miss, and then leave, why not reload and try again?

England says because the ducks would have flown off and there'd be nothing but the surface of the water agitated by their takeoff.

Snare says fair enough, but still that doesn't mean the son is not a psychopathic murderer or has *the potential* to become a psychopathic

murderer and only now that he has the gun in his hands does he realize his true self is not only jokey and inappropriate but also actually
really scary when armed like this and so he blows the father-in-law's
head off and takes off west on a killing spree, Snare says, satisfied
with himself, amused, as he takes a celebratory sip.

They don't seem to notice me across the booth, rubbing my left
shoulder, pausing now and then to down more water, which our
friendly energetic server refreshes. I wonder if I'm also imaginary,
a figment of my own imagination, sitting across from these guys.

I say shit my shoulder suddenly hurts.

It seems like England and Snare are real since they acknowledge
me.

Snare asks if England's story hurt me?

I may have exacerbated a minor weight-lifting injury by going
on a sixteen-mile walking-and-reading session this morning, I say,
and after intoning the words "sixteen-mile walking-and-reading
session" they're asking if I still do that, if I still walk and read to work,
they thought I was biking more, saving time by biking, they thought
I'd be dead by now, hit by a car, a bus, how come you haven't been
hit by a bus yet, they say in unison *how come you haven't been hit by a bus
yet?*

The pain in my shoulder now makes me think the two guys in
front of me are one beast, a codependent couple, essentially, who
mutually enable burdensomeness with beer and talk, and so now sitting there as they talk, riffing on walking and reading, I rub my sore
shoulder and dream about walking and reading that morning.

Three miles to the ten-mile loop and then three miles home,
walking and reading the Penelope section at the end of *Ulysses*, whispering it, listening to its rhythms and melodies, as I walked, trying
to steady myself as bikers and rollerbladers and runners passed every few seconds, the river always to my left as I walked upstream to
the East Falls bridge, crossed it, stood and looked at the water and

thought about nothing, just looked at trees along the banks reflected in the river. I tried to see through the surface to the river bottom especially where it's visible closer to the banks, not deep enough if I decided there and then to jump, but no desire to jump, to end it, life's just starting with a baby in wife's belly.

Once there'd been fire in our bellies we squelched with drink but now there's a baby in wife's belly and she's doing everything in her power not to squelch it. For dinner I've been making low-glycemic masterpieces heavy on dark leafy greens, doing whatever I can to help grow the baby. Lying on our sides in bed I read to the bump the best possible literature I can. Holding my phone to the bump I play songs the prenatal kid might like, melodic songs with a watery feel, instrumentals evoking underwater scenes, doing whatever I can, knowing the kid will be whoever it is, whoever it becomes. With or without prenatal serenades, we'll help it along, he or she, although we envision a boy, see a boy coming into our lives, and then I wonder what will happen if the boy makes friends with a neighborhood kid and together they're like Snare and England? Better like me and whatever book I'm reading, walking and reading, on the streets, in nature, performing the time-tested balancing act between reader and book. At best it's ideal love, reader requires book, book requires reader, together they bring the story to life, the way my wife and I bring our child to life, co-creating the child as I sit in an enormous wooden Viking booth in a Transylvanian bar worthy of the inn from the opening of Kafka's *The Castle* and watch Snare and England co-create the child that is their talk together.

They're defaulting to complaints about students and administrators and their universities in general, the corporate money-making machine known as higher-education institutions. It would make me sick and shaken at a spiritual level to teach where Snare and England have taught for six or seven years. Listening to them talk about their worst students isn't something I can do anymore, so I think about walking and reading and my child en route and my wife asleep on the couch, her body transformed, aqueous, filled with water.

I whisper silent prayers for Oates and Gibson to complicate the dynamics of the one hundred and eighth celebration of Bloomsday, to signal with their presence the next round of the night once they step over the corpse shot in the back of the head by Snare to avenge England's hijacking of whatever Snare had wanted to say about how we're sitting ducks in terms of sensitivity and psychic trauma whenever we consider the success of peers. Whenever we think about someone we know publishing their novel manuscript or receiving good reviews or winning an award or grant or fellowship or teaching job, we're ducks sitting out in the open. The father's name is Envy and the son's name is Spite. They train their rifles on us and never miss whenever we're transformed into sitting ducks by thinking about the success of a writer we know.

For the most part I ignore the American literary publishing industry, so I feel it to a lesser degree. I favor classics and European, East Asian, and South American novels in translation and trust myself more than I trust the American literary publishing industry. Smoke signals from the American literary publishing industry don't make sense. They're hasty and shallow, overwhelmed by marketing and ambition. Thanks to the internet and email and word-processing applications, everyone's writing novels and sending them to overwhelmed agents and their assistants.

I wonder if I would have been a writer if it weren't so easy to manage long complicated documents on a computer. Would I have worked on a typewriter, fussing with ribbons, carefully scissoring horizontal scraps of paper with rewritten lines to paste over text in need of improvement? Would I have put in the work if the processes were so inefficient? I probably would have handwritten and then worked that way, handwriting notes in the margins of the manuscript, getting it all right before sitting down to type.

Inefficiencies had kept the number of writers reasonably low, but now there's no barrier between desire and action. If someone wants to write something and send it to agents they can do it if they find the time to sit in a chair and write, so people sit in chairs and write and send fiction to agents and editors of journals. They apply in record numbers to MFA programs. In record numbers they apply to art colonies and for fellowships and grants and prizes, and they do so because it's so easy to hear about these opportunities and submit to them. It once was covert information, the application process and deadlines and existence of opportunities available. Agents now found online accept email queries and every day receive hundreds if not thousands of messages from applicants asking to please consider representing me and the attached manuscript, thank you so much for your consideration. An onslaught of ambition, queries, synopses, brief bios, sincere thanks. There's no other way to describe what's happened thanks to the internet except *onslaught*. I suppose I contribute to it too. I suppose I am among the hundreds of thousands of writers in the world, all writing fiction, mostly genre fiction inspired by blockbusters involving wizards, vampires, and sadomasochists, some of it literary, a genre in itself.

The literary fiction genre believes it's not a genre, despite rules of engagement, to ensure connection with readers, learned at graduate school programs. Tens of thousands of applicants apply to graduate school as though certification is a prerequisite for writing. At these graduate schools they round the corners of what makes their writing their own. They listen to and provide critiques of stories and novel excerpts, for the most part offering and receiving advice on how to *round the corners* of their prose, domesticate whatever's in it that might be a wild cat, instead of suggesting how to return a domesticated element to its natural habitat, accentuating everything wild and unique. Of the thousands who nod their heads at suggestions deemed helpful, not suppressive but supportive, of the tens of thousands who submit themselves to graduate program writing workshops, a handful live the dream of seeing their work accepted by publications that champion fiction held down by the weight of convention.

Only if held down by *the weight of convention* can the casual reader be elevated by the story. The weight of convention lets the casual reader's spirit ascend. The reader's imagination lifts the weight of convention and this effort is the reader's reward. The weight of convention resembles Nautilus machines on which readers are accustomed to exercising their imaginations. There's something fascist about aiming for a conventional instead of a peculiar ideal. Yet writers submit to it on purpose, in complete possession of their cognitive faculties.

They lift the weights of convention and say they're stronger for it, but what else might they say? Went to graduate school, came back confused and weakened by self-consciousness? Instead of deeply imagining what they're writing they're thinking too much about writing as they write, thoughts about writing always in the way of what they're writing, the weight of convention a blackout shade over their sight they're forced to throw off, write by hand as fast as they can on as much caffeine as possible until they can see through the pen, a periscope cracking the surface of the notebook pages to better see the world they're imagining, see something that doesn't exist and describe it so it does.

They talk about writing like it involves weights and measures, combustible reactions, life or death at the hands of craft-related equations like "pressure reveals character," when it's a simple magic trick involving seeing something that doesn't exist and describing it so it does. Describing something that doesn't exist so others see it too. That's all it is. No big deal. The weight of convention like the weight of the corpse of the father-in-law Snare murdered on a whim. Only we at the Viking booth see the corpse since no one comes to clean brains from door, no one trips upon entering or exiting thanks to the headless lifeless corpse of England's hunter.

The pressure of the situation increases.

I become progressively agitated the longer it's just me and Snare and England.

I keep eyes on the door as it opens and closes behind small groups, lone guys popping in for one-and-done drinks or carry-out six packs, as Snare and England inflate a bubble of talk.

Head in hands lets me subtly insert the terminal digits of index fingers in ears. Through fingertips subtly inserted in ears I hear them discuss students, non-canonical lit, books I've never heard of, books they thought "looked interesting" while browsing their university library. I'm getting irritated as third wheel not really interested in discussion about such an interesting book. What would be *interesting* at this moment would be for some maniac to run through the barroom to shish kabob with a long spear the skulls of my two friends here. That might shut their yaps. Chances of that happening are slim, and I suppose I don't want their skulls pierced. They can't help who they are, same as I can't help who I am, despite often trying to help who I am.

Walking and reading is how I help who I am, a positive endeavor without drawbacks. Writing is how I help who I am, and to a lesser degree drinking is how I help who I am. I'm always trying to help who I am, writing, reading, drinking, walking, exercising, trying to have my wits about me.

If I've dug my fingers too far into my ears I won't be able to get them out before Jonathan David Grooms's arrival. If I try too hard to extract them, I'll injure my fingertips, which I use daily for writing and working and other tasks, or I'll somehow injure my brain. I'll learn American Sign Language to converse with wife and child but fingertips will be disjointed and odd-shaped so I'll inadvertently sign odd phrases. Hereafter I shall pay the price for impatience: crooked fingers, nonfunctional ears, stabbed brain.

What's that called, the part of the brain closest to the ears?

I remove fingertips from ears without trouble. Snare and England talk about a book I've never heard of. I thumb a question into my phone about the part of the brain closest to the ear. The first offering is about how scientists have discovered that the right temporo-parietal junction, just behind the right ear, is a moral compass that controls how we judge other people's behavior. It lights up when we think about other people's behaviors, when we judge them for good or ill, and these judgments can be affected with the application of magnets. Seems like quackery to me, old-fashioned magnetism, but the study suggests there's more to our moral sense than early philosophical indoctrination, or how we were raised, or what we learned in church. Our brain's biology has something to do with it too, which is maybe what I was trying to do with fingers in ears. Flick a switch that controls judgment. Disable that function. In general it seems like the beer has been making my right temporo-parietal junction fire too rapidly in judgment so I tried to spear that part of my brain and while doing so imagined spearing them like shish kabobs?

I am the one who needs to stand in judgment, clearly. I'm sure my time will come. Now it's best to sit back and relax and enjoy some calm before the storm.

The most beautiful day of the year so far, summer officially launched, the complete vernal experience ahead, the change of season seems new every time, the environmental epitome of the writing cliché *strange yet familiar*, the patient rotation of the seasons the model for everyone seeking to overcome impatience.

There's a Kafka quotation in *The Blue Octavo Notebooks*, a collection of fragments and aphorisms published by Exact Change, owned by Damon and Naomi of Galaxie 500, that has something to do with impatience and the Garden of Eden, with paradise.

Because of impatience we were forced from paradise, because of impatience we cannot return, something like that, I can't remember, or maybe I remember it well enough.

I can't ask Snare or England about it. They've probably read *The Trial* and "The Metamorphosis," the story not the collection of stories named after the story. They're writers and yet when someone says *Great Wall of China* they think of a wall visible from outer space along the northern border of China, but when I hear *Great Wall of China* I think about the Kafka story and the Kafka collection. I think about Kafka and China. I see both a book and a wall at once.

I think of the Kafka story but I can hardly remember what it's about. It's important that I think about it even if I can't remember what it's about. It's about a messenger. It's all there in my memory ready for release when I re-read the words. I handled the old green hardback octavo earlier in the day. When I get home I'll kiss sleeping super-pregnant wife and then read that story about a messenger and the Great Wall of China.

How can it be important if I can't remember it? It made such an impression that now I can't remember it? The book in the blood, not in the brain?

What was the quotation about impatience? It's impatience that's the worst, impatience against which the seasons rotate?

I don't ask Snare and England as they layer language over one another in a way they must find pleasurable, not completing each other's sentences so much as jousting, each sentence charging the other's sentence, each utterance heard and not heard. Impossible, I think, for someone who is neither Snare nor England to listen to such speech. Thankfully we have phones on which Kafka quotations appear when search queries are entered, so I enter "Kafka impatience quote." Seconds later I scroll down as I read:

> *There are two main human sins from which all the others derive: impatience and indolence. It was because of impatience*

that they were expelled from Paradise, it is because of indolence
that they do not return. Yet perhaps there is only one major sin:
impatience. Because of impatience they were expelled, because
of impatience they do not return.

I never would have remembered *indolence*, that wasn't in my memory. I only remembered *impatience*, not *indolence*. I wouldn't associate *indolence* and *impatience*. Beyond their physical resemblance I wouldn't think of them existing on the same plane. I suppose it's about control, about letting what you want arrive in time. Letting it come to you. Kafka's practice of sitting late at night and letting the world open up as he sat at his desk. I thumb in the search terms "Kafka sit patiently quote" and seconds later I find it:

It is not necessary to leave the house. Sit at your table and listen.
Don't even listen, just wait. Don't even wait, just be solitary and
still. The world will present itself to you for its unmasking, it can
do nothing else, it will writhe in ecstasy at your feet.

I always took this as writing advice but it sounds like meditation, the world obliged to come like a loyal dog if you're patient. We're waiting for Jonathan David Grooms as the most beautiful day of the year ends and the most beautiful night begins. I wonder what are the chances of anyone *writhing in ecstasy* tonight, especially if we sit patiently in silence and wait, although it would be hard not to listen to the jukebox and bursts of noise, expelled breath conveying language I'd prefer not to hear. I would like a moment of silence in the barroom. I would like the jukebox to blast some John Cage. I would like to hear the complexity of sound mapped in crayon scrawl and stared at until the center of the page ignites and there's silence instead of smoke.

XIII.

I visit the notorious bathroom and return to Oates and Gibson opposite Snare and England in the Viking booth in the back room. I slide next to England, back to the wall, across from Oates, who sits like a silver bishop on a swirling indefinite mess of a chessboard, the personification of a moment of clarity. He's as freshly shaven as an early 1960s movie star, skin white and pink and freckled, deeply moisturized, hair emerging from winter brown en route to summer orange, eyes amber and clear in darkened sockets. He always selects an India Pale Ale and downs the first as though extinguishing whatever conflagration inside him accounts for his complexion.

Gibson seems to have avoided the sun for consecutive summers. He's cultivating some stubble that since his daughter's birth arrives grayer each time it grows out, which makes him seem older than anyone at the table when he's not much older than England.

Snare the youngest, then England, Gibson, Oates, me, each a year or two apart.

I think Gibson and Oates and England seem older than I do but I never see myself telling a story, ordering a drink, sliding into the booth after I've stepped outside to bum a smoke or visited the bathroom. It's possible I seem older than everyone, older by far. It's possible no one can believe how old I've become. If surveyed, they might say I look fifty or flatter me and say no more than thirty, the range between thirty and fifty. I probably look thirty-five and feel younger or older, none of which will matter once the child is born and for two years at least we relate his age in terms of months. At this point, for me, age only tracks how long my body has existed. After a certain age, time alive is less important than how life has been lived.

It's hard to say how much Oates and Gibson have had to drink. They often pre-game at Oates's place, sipping a beer or a gin and tonic while playing with Oates's baby girl, or they stop somewhere along their bike ride through the city. Gibson lives a little to the north and Oates lives a little to the west of the city's center, whereas the bar is more than a little to the southeast of the city's center, so on the way they may have stopped to prepare themselves for a situation where they might not know everyone, since they don't know everyone as well as I know everyone, even as well as England knows everyone.

I'm the only one who knows them all equally, more or less, somehow. I've read all their writing in the past years, met their spouses, been to their places, high-fived their children, pet their pets, eaten meals they've prepared, and shared at least a hundred beers with each of them over time. Excessive consumption of beer in another's presence forms a bond. After four beers as many as five years ago we may have considered ourselves friends. When I first met these guys five or six or seven years ago, from the beginning it was like we sat together at this table except really no more than once or twice a year do these four sit down together with me and with Lao, the wild card in all this, someone who does not spend much time with anyone other than me or England, mainly due to proximity, but also he doesn't have a bike because Lao either doesn't know how to ride one or doesn't want to endanger himself as he bikes home.

Neither Gibson nor Oates are their family's primary breadwinner the way Lao is. If Gibson or Oates drink too much in celebration of the one hundred and eighth anniversary of Bloomsday and fail to negotiate the old trolley tracks left in the pavement on Eleventh Street when biking home, if a car door opens and sends them flying through the air as their bike sprawls without rider, smushed against an unsuspecting car door, if they lose control and fall off and a car runs over an important part of them, on and on, if tragedy strikes, their wives will manage without them, each holding full-time jobs and bringing in more money than their husbands. But Lao's wife is an illustrator who sells quirky drawings at craft fairs and online. Her primary job is to save the Guardian family tens of thousands of dollars in daycare while raising their son.

Everyone has daughters except for Lao whose feisty blond sunflower-headed son loves trains, a three-year-old, so Lao as the sole breadwinner of his family stays off bikes since riding a bike increases the possibility of tragic injury. There's really no need for Lao to ride a bike since he rarely travels beyond two nearby neighborhood bars, whereas Gibson and Oates are more rangy when active despite having daughters as old as Lao's son. All these fiction writers with toddlers at home, unlike Snare and England without children, England without pets, not even a fish, maybe a desiccated spider plant and a tiny cactus on a windowsill, whereas Snare has a wife and two dogs, and Gibson has wife and daughter, and Oates has wife and daughter and the cutest little miniature pug-type thing, some Asian breed that overproduces folds of skin across its smushed little snout face, and this dog, Ronald, informally known as Ron, allows Oates entry into worlds the rest of us don't so often explore, not having a dog such as Ron.

Snare has two dogs but lives in the suburbs and his dogs are old and stay in his fenced-in backyard. He doesn't take them to the dog run at the park and make friends there with other dog owners who invite him to barbecues or drinks. But Oates, armed with Ron, with or without his daughter, are a fearsome duo. Freckled and straight-backed and proud, Oates stands erect as a sight-hound himself, a lighthouse casting for vessels distressed on the troubled seas of the park, charming vessels attracted to the bright white erotic light he and Ron emit, and in this way his territory extends. The other married men, the rest of us, even sole bachelor England, aren't compelled to stray, to roam, or if compelled we resist, don't do more than engage in subtle admiration, each year more awed and baffled by youth, each year defining youth more broadly, now considering a thirty-year-old young, a twenty-five-year-old a child, experiencing more and more each year poignant separation from a world that not so long ago had seemed to overflow with opportunity, or at least had seemed potentially in play.

Pregnant wife on couch like a turtle flipped over on its shell. Never an opportunity to take the houseplants for a stroll around the neighborhood to the park and meet people there, not that I'd befriend the people I met, that's not something I see happening, whereas Oates, despite the illusion of uprightness, suggests that opportunities abound. There's something about him like the smiling red-headed freckled doll that seems at peace in the corner until it reveals itself as satanic and eats your face. There's something sneakily devilish about him unlike Snare whose devils ride out in the open on either shoulder, like faithful parrots, obvious companions, there for all to see. But with Oates there's also a sense that those devils would never turn on you and feed on your face. His devils have other meals in mind, I think, or so Oates suggests, never going into detail. I suppose it's possible he prefers to perpetuate the suggestion that there's more there than there is. The suggestion of something more is all he wants, the suggestion he's been a bad boy, that he retains the right to revel in selfishness whereas I believe he only fantasizes about opportunities seized and otherwise lives a devoted, staid home life, does dishes and straightens the area where his daughter plays and puts away crayons scattered over floor as the part of his brain engaged when he writes activates daydream autopilot mode about simple carnal workouts with embodiments of beauty who admire Ron and pet him in the park to the point of overstimulation, not only of Ron but of all who witness Ron petted with such intensity that the folds of skin cascading across the little dog's back and neck and snout retract to reveal a handheld canine pleasure device. All those there, Oates for sure, hope that embodiments of beauty take Ron in their arms and retreat to benches and hike skirts, Oates attending to domestic duties fantasizing about his little pet in the hands of embodiments of beauty lightly perspiring, wearing jaunty skirts, applying Ron to themselves in a way that could only be called *conspicuous.*

I've never felt that Oates had it in for me, or was critical of me, or didn't have my back, or wouldn't give me the benefit of the doubt. He's an open-hearted and loyal friend, but his thought dreams, as Dylan called them, might stray in such a way to mean trouble should his suggestions ever turn out true. He exists in the hypothetical, as potential, as possibility, the man across from me in the giant booth, his back to the room, sitting where I had sat, and now he seems distracted.

He never seems totally present but his presence isn't required for him to influence the room. Some need their body animated with all their spirit, the blood and brainwaves that move them, always un-self-consciously *on.* All of us at the table always reserve some of ourselves, sometimes most of ourselves, holding back, storing whatever we can store, not participating so much as observing. There's always some awkwardness when someone accustomed to sitting, writing, and reading steps on the stage of life and realizes there's no such thing as a rough first draft, a scrawl for the writer's eyes only, an experiment to see what's in the well, excavation that can be panned for something precious therein. Everything else might be worthless gravel but a phrase glints for a second, a phrase that once its potential is revealed by application of sufficient attention can become a seed from which something inspired grows. But what if there's no opportunity to apply sufficient attention to a moment and moments are smeared by sound and movement and fancy beer? Instead of precise attentive calculated moments it's rangy improvisational interaction, more in tune with the pace of things, and yet here we are, five writer friends full-speed ahead, the prevailing wind filling our sails and setting us across a night's inebriation, the crosscurrent of speech rising and falling with drinks, our Viking booth now a worthy vessel, one for all and all for one, each the other's vassal as we journey toward some continental abstraction of the New World, a vast, inchoate, fraught, figurative territory ahead wherein, like El Dorado or the Fountain of Youth, we hope to discover successful completion of the dream that first set us in this direction.

So many years ago we began with a dream of publication, a dream of interdependent life and text, life as it presented itself to us and texts we wrote and texts we read might form a holy trinity, the three major masts of our vessel as it careens en route to whatever remnant exists of that first dream. We approached from various directions, each coming toward it differently, men between the ages of 29 and 40, each concerned with telling different stories, different ways of telling stories, concerned with differentiation, each at this Viking Vessel running different flags up the poles, different standards: Oates more descended from Stendhal than Gibson descended from Orwell than England descended from the Great American Richards than Snare descended from every firebrand whoever burned out before achieving canonical recognition. But it's unfair to reduce each writer to a primary descendent. It reduces who they are. It also requires me to know everything they've written and know the work of every foundational writer of past centuries.

I might note similarities among past writers and the writing of my friends but I shouldn't reduce Oates's writing to the tilt-a-whirl dynamics of *The Red and the Black*, even if there's a swashbuckling element to his best stuff, like his sentences cut and slip ahead and back across the page. His sentences seem intent on cutting the pages he writes to shreds, tearing at the fabric of reality between reader and writer. Sharp, honed, dynamic, effortless, precise, quick, cunning, graceful, dexterous, deft, these words come to mind when reading his stuff. I picture his narrators as Errol Flynn playing Robin Hood in tights and little boots flared at the calves, a tunic that at times almost looks like a miniskirt. Some people when they first meet Oates think he isn't quite straight, an assumption supported by the swashbuckling tone of his writing. It's not that he's gay, I say when asked, just he's *Californian*. Oates isn't a surfer or a gangbanger or glitzy ditz and so he confuses them.

He looks like someone who had once been a priest, sat with hundreds discussing sins, studied a book he no longer owns, dedicated himself to one thing for so many years and then bailed on it. There's a sense with Oates he's on his second life. He checks his words before he releases them, ensuring their point of origin isn't his previous life. It would be wonderful to discover that Oates is in the Witness Protection Program. Ratted out a Californian drug ring and now on the East Coast goes by Addison Oates, far from home, out of harm's way, although who knows how long the protection will last, at any minute the doors may open, shots ring out in Oates's direction, and we'll be covered in spilled beer and blood. It seems inevitable that someone will come in tonight and splatter us in beer and blood after riddling us with bullets, although this is just a projection of anticipatory anxiety, the sense that the all-mighty Jonathan David Grooms himself will soon intone the final series of affirmations, an answer to the unasked question of life itself, and then shake hands and sign books before Lao escorts him to a cab to take him where we wait to receive him. His every move must be like that, his every outing a celebration with extraneous seats at every table for admirers.

We always figured we could make our dreams come true as long as we didn't consider them dreams. If we consider our dreams the consequences of hard work and we work hard we will settle into our rightful home. But it seems that talent and hard work aren't enough, although it's possible we aren't sufficiently talented and don't work hard enough, in which case we all seem to think we may need a fortuitous association to push our vessels ashore.

XIV.

The way Oates treats his first drink, it's clear he's eager to celebrate Bloomsday. Gibson too seems primed for a blowout. Previous years had been quiet, as though we were saving ourselves for tonight, or maybe it had something to do with Gibson, Oates, and Lao having newborns and then toddlers at home. They've settled into parenthood, routines are set, household management roles established, plus it doesn't hurt when Gibson informs us that his wife and daughter and Oates's wife and daughter are camping on Gibson's wife's parents' property in the Poconos. Morning involves no energetic curious needy children, no superhuman toddler monsters practicing new words, constructing sentences, narrating dreams as though they're real, parroting their parents, the television, lyrics of songs, mimicking everything at max volume until it becomes who they are.

Gibson seems like the oldest because he has the oldest child even if he's only a little older than England and Lao and younger than Oates and me. England with his bald head, Lao with his blond head, Oates with his red head, Snare with his mostly brown but also somewhat white head since his scalp can be seen through gelled hair, me with my shaggy brown head, Gibson with his progressively graying head. Because Gibson seems the oldest with his gray head and initial exposure to the stages of pediatric development he's granted more authority, also because he seems more solid than the rest of us. He may be in worse shape in every possible way but he doesn't let on, except when discussing writing, in particular when he refers to himself as an artist.

The word *artist* comes loaded with connotations beyond those of the word *writer*, which is of course a subset of *artist* but most writers feel uncomfortable calling themselves *artists* since it took time to become comfortable declaring themselves *writers*, as though self-identification as *writer* requires a certain number of words written, pages written, stories and novels written, publications, stories and novels read, experience gained, lessons learned. After a time, there's no way you'd call yourself anything other than *writer* since the term describes what you do. Once you are what you do, you earn the term *writer*, whereas *artist* as a self-identifying term lacks specificity, suggests flightiness, suggests someone touched and almost magical, holes in skulls letting in the elements, the light and wind and smells enter through thin cerebral skin, mix in brain and blend, emitted as art. I never self-conceive as an artist. Whenever someone suggests I'm an artist at most I respond hmm yeah I guess.

Visual artists I've known spend less time alone than I do, their work is often collaborative and physical, like carpentry or construction, installation art, video art, mixed media, plus there's always a sense that some artists are in fact bullshit artists. But then some artists create something beautiful or odd or peculiar or particular that suggests real magic to what they do. Artists and their artistry like wizards and their wizardry. They don't look like bullshit artists who look and act and talk like artists. Wizardry artists only have artistry up their sleeves.

Gibson refers to himself as an artist more than any writer I have ever met and since he looks unlike a bullshit artist when he calls himself an artist it suggests inner turmoil and ambition and anxiety and awareness that needs release. Because he's a writer-type artist he releases the neurological and emotional and psychological and intellectual components of his artistry as words. He seems broken down more than most about the process of stringing words onto pages, maybe because he seems less expressive of inward turmoil et cetera he's more worried about how one goes about putting words on pages. Because he doesn't seem to release pent-up energies, especially toxic or neurotic energies, in daily life, his writing has become therapy, whereas everyone else, particularly Snare and Lao and me and Oates and England, in that order descending from Snare to England to Gibson, release pent-up toxic or neurotic energies as a consequence of who we are, how we act, and writing is part of the release. Writing is one among many actions and activities, outward expression of peculiarities, toxins, neuroses, emotion manifested as anger, sorrow, regret, awe, love. But more than anyone else I know Gibson seems better able to control himself, which extends to his prose.

He talks about not knowing how to write a novel whereas he knows how to write a story. He knows the mechanics, feels like he controls that realm of existence to a satisfactory degree, or so Gibson has more than once said, but when it comes to novels he's not sure, has less experience, has encountered fewer problems and seen fewer solutions.

Lao and Gibson argued about it one night: the unconventional language-headed experimentalist who's read everything said over and over as Gibson talked about not knowing how to write a novel that there's no way to write a novel. Every novel in fact presents a novel solution, every novel is its own thing, particularly great novels, Lao said. Language assumes the overall form it requires to take over time as the novel grows. The form can't be imposed. The novel's form emerges from writing the novel. The novel has its own life if it's a good novel.

Lao can be critical and expert in his pronouncements as a reader even if he hasn't yet lived up to his talent and ambition as a writer. He directs his talent and ambition toward a target unrelated to major New York City publishing houses and so his mind remains more open maybe since he targets small presses and wants nothing to do with the Majors, as he calls New York City publishers. Not that he wants nothing to do with a Major but he wants to be minor. His definition of minor doesn't mean lesser so much as individual, particular, unique, unable to influence someone without that influenced writer being forever considered derivative of the work of Lao Guardian.

Per Lao, a major writer's distinguishing feature is their indistinguishable influence. Franzen, for example, is a major writer: if you intentionally mimic his writing style, it won't seem like a particular style has been aped. But if you write like Wallace, watch out. Therefore Franzen is a major writer, Wallace a minor writer. Again, major and minor don't confer value. If anything minor is better than major, Lao often argues after too many beers.

Lao wants to be a minor writer whereas Gibson wants to be a major writer, or more so, Gibson wants to write a conventional novel he can sell that lets him live the life of a writer who writes conventional novels he can sell to support his family and his future writing. He places more pressure on his writing because he wants it to fulfill this ideal of the Majors, as Lao would say, whereas Lao and Snare to an extent don't think this way, whereas I believe in improving what I'm working on until it seems like it can no longer be improved. I believe in the habit, its psychological and emotional necessity. Without it I became inhospitable. Internal climate roils and I storm more often than not if I don't maintain my precious writing habit.

For Gibson, this doesn't suffice. He wants to know how to write a novel, and I know how to write a novel because I've written several but because they're unpublished novels, unpublished and apparently *unpublishable* novels, I have no authority when it comes to how to write a novel. My writing at this point is about writing and writing alone. I try to keep it simple, try not to worry about structure which I don't always trust, instead I only want to write. That's my sole desire when it comes to writing, or so I tell myself. And the world so far has responded that I can write all I want. Be extraordinarily productive, an industry unto thyself. But extraordinary productivity doesn't mean readers will want to read my writing. Because among us I'm considered a writer who writes as a vocation at best, a vendetta against the world at worst, religious observance at best, obsessive pathological disorder at worst, I often feel like what I say holds no weight, so I listen more than I talk. I let what's said sink in so it might come out when I write. Whatever they say will never be read so it doesn't matter if I filter it all through me and type it up.

I consider these people friends even if they discount me because I haven't gone to graduate school for fiction and profess no real qualms about the challenges of writing novels because they think, or so I've thought, that I don't know enough about writing, that I haven't been to Iowa or Syracuse, haven't studied with Marilynne Robinson or Frank Conroy or Ethan Canin or James Alan McPherson or George Saunders or Mary Karr or Arthur Flowers, that because I haven't studied with anyone other than a thousand closely read novels and stories and essays what I have to say means nothing, not to mention also admittedly that I have little to say about it because obstacles I encounter I overcome through intuition developed over years of reading and writing.

I'm not all that old but I've been reading serious lit and trying to write it for longer than the younger kids at the bar have been alive. The fully formed and not so fully clothed woman with tattoos sitting at the corner of the bar closest to our booth wasn't yet born when I started writing in high school. If she were twenty-one or twenty-two that would be true. Something must be seriously wrong with my writing if I've been doing it for so many years with so little success. Twenty-something years of writing and only a few stories posted on a weird little lit site seems like an odd way to spend one's life. The bulk of my life spent reading and writing, fully engaged with the process at the expense of everything else, and all I have to show for it are all these novels that some may consider carefully copyedited "early drafts." I never fail to correct typos and pass over the language dozens of times to ensure a certain aerodynamics, a smoothness, as the eye crosses and scrolls down the pages, but I seldom reorganize everything or reinvent characters to increase motivation if they seem insufficiently goal-orientated/desire-driven. Seldom do I redirect their course until they charge with equal yet opposite energy toward opposing characters. Seldom do I perform the post-compositional craft work needed to meet the standards of the genre known as contemporary conventional American literary fiction.

I do some of it, of course. I work on the manuscript for months after the first draft seems complete, but I never restart the novel from scratch. I don't cut up pages and rearrange them so they're all over the room, color-coded so I might layer fragments together that make thematic sense. I don't do that because I've done it once or twice. I have excessively revised my writing. I felt in fact like I only became a writer when I started seriously revising what I wrote. Revision is the key to writing, not at first but a few years after the initial infatuation with the act of composition.

At first I wrote stories by hand and then left them in notebooks for months and then typed them up and left them as they were, not reworking or making many changes, the manuscript like the impression of a dream, abstract, foreboding, often surreal, but I never revised. Not until I started improving the language, treating every sentence like a puzzle to solve for clarity, efficiency, aerodynamics, and grace, for texture and timbre, did I begin to become a writer. Not until I'd worked on the prose and reorganized stories for better entryways in the opening pages, for more substantial, fulfilling endings, did I become a writer. This was writing, revising was writing, composing was a fraction and revising was the rest.

Writing is a combination of composition and revision. For the first few years I had only composed, which is why I had never really thought of myself as a writer, but once I began revising I began to think of myself as a writer because I was finally *actually writing*, that is, I was composing and revising, championing revision over composition.

I thought of myself as a writer if not an artist since I sat at a computer moving words around, so fully engaged that hours disappeared as I worked to revise new raw material I'd composed. This was an experience I wanted more than anything, to exist outside time as I worked, to enter what I was working on to such a degree that I existed in that world for a while.

The activity was free, had no real side effects, cost nothing, had minimal environmental impact as long as you didn't print up a new draft with each minor revision. At most the only danger is that immersion in fictional worlds consisting of carefully considered language makes you less able to improvise when interacting with human beings whose dialogue you don't control. At worst after spending too many hours immersed in fictional worlds you might have some trouble existing in the so-called real world. At worst you become *a little weird*, lose some fluency when it comes to interacting with people, but that all depends on who you are to begin with, and in general I've never been all that fluent when interacting with people so the change wouldn't be notable, plus no one would notice because I've never been too committed to spending time with people. I'm committed to spending time alone in a way that seldom feels lonely because I'm reading or writing, interacting with people and worlds, and even when I feel the need to stop being so sedentary I take a book with me, not hiding from the world but interacting with it as a reader walking through it.

Immersion in worlds generated by reading is more important to me than immersion in the unbounded world, the one in which we live, the common denominator world, and of course I live in the common world but I also live with imagination committed to the skewed yet recognizable worlds of fiction. I feel most immersed in the common world when most immersed in the parallel world of fiction, either as a reader or a writer. After half an hour of composing/revising, sitting at the computer in solitude and silence, I notice I've not been aware of sitting and writing, I've been on automatic pilot, body erased, spirit pure, which makes writing addictive, deep concentration, active productive daydream, lucid dreaming traced with language, a state achieved through sitting and thinking, sitting and imagining, related to meditation albeit with a byproduct of words.

I don't know how to say it in a way that Gibson understands: there's no secret to writing a novel, no code, no formula. Novels are written by sitting and imagining and smearing hours with words, revised and reordered if necessary, reshaped to tell the story in a way that reproduces something like that state of sitting and imagining for someone else, a stranger, the writer in the guise of a reader. I don't see why someone might want to control the process from the beginning, have a plan, a list of desired effects, themes, plots, subplots, conflicts among the characters, each with pasts that motivate present actions, each in conflict with one other, all resolved at the end with a proverbial tidy bow.

I don't understand tidy bow writing. It seems less like the finishing touches on a tasteful, thoughtful gift than total conformity, more like a product than a work of art, or a gift, and yet Gibson is the one among us most concerned with *tidy bow writing* and also the one who self-identifies as artist, even if *tidy bow writing* seems more like craft than art, construction instead of expression.

Gibson should self-ID as *craftsman* because he wants discoveries made in advance during the crafting instead of during the act. If something were at stake for a character it was planned by the author ahead of time because it was required by the form of the highly crafted *tidy bow* literary product that something be at stake for a character, and so something was at stake for a character because of perceived craft prerequisites instead of the propulsion of art, the details unearthed and advanced thanks to imagination and intuition.

Nabokov called his characters "galley slaves." He knew what they were doing and why, which is why his writing so often seems like gorgeous specimens pinned to a board under glass instead of writhing and alive and aloft in flight, wings dusty, perishable, not long for this earth.

I don't need to control my writing the way Gibson does. Writers who need to control their writing look down on those who don't. Those who apply constrictions of craft often attest to not enjoying writing. It's difficult work because they analyze and adjust scenes and characters for effect. They exert far more artifice and as such deem themselves artists instead of craftsmen, whereas another sort of writer releases talent and imagination and intuition (indispensable muscle tied to the imagination strengthened over a lifetime of reading and writing and living), in such a way that an equivalent group of effects are created, sensations certain readers may prefer over what's experienced when reading something tightly crafted.

Chief among the intuitive/ecstatic set of effects is the sense that what's read comes streaked with the natural looseness of life. The story feels real because it doesn't feel controlled the way life itself doesn't feel controlled. Uncontrolled writing proceeds in such a way that seems uncontrolled when really it's controlled by the writer who often lets the language and the story conveyed by it do what they seem like they need to do. I'm the sort of writer who gets out of the way so I can't offer much assistance to Gibson who wants to control his writing and write a novel that ends with a *tidy bow* atop it.

Whenever I say he needs to let the novel write itself he smirks as though I suggested we skinny dip in the river once the bar lets out. Sounds like fun but no way he'll do such a thing.

He wants to control his fictional world the way he controls his so-called real world. Gibson requires something explicit, something tangible to follow, a map, an outline. He needs it planned to ensure he doesn't waste time. Without guidelines he feels lost, and yet he doesn't seem more methodical than anyone else in terms of getting his drink on, other than ordering the cheapest local craft beer available in a bottle, that is, a Kenzinger in a bottle (a dollar cheaper than the same beer on draft). He drinks with the same improvisational furor as everyone else, the same willingness to release himself into the crisscrossing currents of speech, but as an artist, as a writer, he's the most methodical and least productive and most concerned with his future.

A little more each year Gibson has been airing doubts about the future of his writing. Effort has not been rewarded with publication, recognition, validation, alleviation of spirits, tension release, or even adequate production. Gibson says he's been working but not accomplishing, revising more than composing, and what he does accomplish he doesn't deem good enough. Stray stories and sections of a longer project that he does complete don't find homes in publications of merit and he isn't interested in submitting to respectable online or so-called middle- or lower-tier publications, even well-designed lesser known independent print journals. So his work seems stuck despite consistent effort to dislodge it and share it.

He doesn't want to continue wasting time working as hard as he does, not spending time with his toddler daughter because he's working on a writing career going nowhere, he says, that refuses to take flight, as though his writing career had a will of its own and shook its head left and right in defiance and clipped its wings after weighing down its talons with heavy stones. His writing career, once a fledgling eagle, is in the process of plucking feathers and butchering itself and offering itself to all those with a rotisserie oven. Gibson's writing goose, essentially, is cooked, or so he says these days after a few bottles of the cheapest local craft beer available.

Now at the booth he grills Snare and England about what they've been up to, as Oates and I look on. Gibson controls the conversation the way he controls his writing. He asks good questions of Snare and England, and he interrupts when they go on too long with their responses.

Oates meanwhile cranes his long white neck so he can see as much of the bar as possible, unhappy with his seat, his back to the room. He will try to sit where I'm sitting or where Snare or England sit, as soon as possible, but all that's yet to come. For now the five of us settle in for what should be about an hour until Lao arrives with Grooms, an hour for the five of us to unite, like the fingers of a fist, before we impress upon Grooms the importance of this meeting, its significance, the night Jonathan David Grooms celebrated the one hundred and eighth anniversary of Bloomsday with Kevin Snare, John England, Addison Oates, Francis Gibson, Lao Guardian, and Throop Roebling, a historic evening, maybe even *an* historic evening.

XV.

I've lost count of how many hefeweizens I've had, four or five, at this point it begins to slip. I haven't downed them fast and they're not as strong as other styles. Effects of higher alcohol levels are visible in Snare and England who drink India Pale Ale, at least seven percent alcohol, maybe more, brewed at first for long journeys on ships, not a fragile citrusy cloudy drink brewed by ancient German monks, the landlubber beer extraordinaire, best enjoyed lazing atop a haystack on a warm autumn afternoon. What everyone other than Gibson and I drink is a rich deep amber, low carbonation so it seems almost oily, tastes spiced, a trace of nutmeg and cloves, a subtle aftertaste of roses and salt, perhaps a hint of crusty sweatsocks, so unlike the Heineken, Michelob, and Budweiser of yore.

Three relatively new and arguably good things about this time in the history of the planet: craft beer, on-demand streaming video consumed on flat-screen high-def TVs, smart phones. No wonder no one reads serious literary fiction and literature.

The representative modern posture is someone slouched over their phone. Tall lanky guy at busy intersection slouched over phone getting directions from a maps app. Girl with long hair hanging down around either side of phone to protect anyone from reading what she texts to someone special. Older woman holding phone close to face, hunting/pecking as she slouches over the ubiquitous device. At home the television connects to on-demand movies and television series, hundreds of entertaining edifying documentaries about obsessives who make a name for themselves as puppeteers or sushi cooks or race car drivers or rappers or Reggae legends. The world at every turn offers so much information it fractures attention, makes you interested in everything, triggers an encyclopedic gene that makes you want to know a little about everything. One thing made absolutely clear is that documentaries about individuals are only made about obsessives, obsessives become encyclopedia entries, whereas generalist appreciators with fractured interests whirling among everything available, artistic jacks of all trades with literary, photo, music, and visual-art projects thanks to programs on laptops are electronic dilettantes with interests and activities dispersed like an army fighting on too many fronts. They're not the subjects of documentaries. With interests and activities dispersed they begin to feel overwhelmed, overloaded, unable to keep up with everything they've started, unable to finish anything they've started, unable to remember where they've saved everything they've started, unable to remember the passwords, the imaginary obligation of all these projects and activities online teams up to sink their spirits, so they slouch over phones, reading updates and tweets as they sit at the bar at a weekday happy hour or early on a Saturday night in mid-June, liking and retweeting, sharing and favoriting, building up e-karma as they indulge in craft beers, taking them for granted now, numbed by the choices on the board, the styles, the goblets and glasses drawn next to the names of the beers, not to mention the price and alcohol by volume. The only response to all this activity, all these outlets for expression online, all these choices in terms of tasty intoxicants, is to overindulge in what's available.

I only stop thinking about how everyone's slouched over phones and start listening to what's being said when Oates starts talking about someone he knew at Yaddo who spent some time with Grooms at McDowell and after enough wine told Oates all about Grooms. It wasn't a story so much as a suggestion that Grooms had expectations that the woman who relayed the story had not expected. She hadn't expected his expectations and had no expectation of fulfilling his expectations. She'd only just gotten to know him. His novels and stories she'd read and liked for the most part, the way most people for the most part like his writing, and because of the writing she was interested for the most part in taking him to her little cabin in the woods, but she didn't quite like him as a person enough and didn't quite like his writing enough to fulfill his expectations.

There was no question what he wanted to do because he was putting her in a position and was attempting to do it, she said, says Oates, and when she refused he responded that if she let him she would know true pleasure and they would be that much closer and would always remember it, or so Oates says the woman said Grooms had said. She didn't want an unforgettable experience if it involved what he wanted to do, not that she hadn't done what he'd wanted to do. She essentially told Oates she wasn't about to give it up to the man right this minute most likely reading aloud the forty-page stream of Molly Bloom's consciousness.

Oates says he couldn't tell whether this woman was coming on to him. They'd downed too much wine and she seemed ready for anything. Oates says he couldn't help thinking and most likely telepathically suggesting to the woman, a well-established, youngish short-story writer in her own right, married and the mother of two young boys, that he wanted to see if he could do what Jonathan David Grooms had apparently failed to do, a man who rarely if ever was rejected, at least in terms of things he wrote.

Snare says maybe he wants to remember what rejection feels like. He must have been rejected at one time, Snare says, and being rejected in bed revives those memories so he can access them when writing.

Gibson says it's all about dashed hopes, all writing is about dashed hopes isn't it, all of us have dashed hopes, all of us started out wanting to be Jonathan David Grooms and instead we're living off dashed hopes, trying to talk ourselves into thinking that dashed hopes are noble.

Oates says anyway I was thinking in an immoral competitive way that if I can do this thing with this woman I'll have achieved an abstract victory over a writer who in every other way has bested me. I was thinking along those lines but when I pressed her about what had happened in the end, no pun, Oates says, she changed the subject, which made me think Grooms had succeeded. Jonathan David Grooms knows as well as anyone the importance of obstacles, of conflict, in stories, and so when the story of one's life proceeds through too many wide-open doors what can you do but impede progress so there's a degree of difficulty and something achieved feels like a legitimate success, Oates says.

The good thing, I say, we all for the most part still have it in front of us. It's better to strive for that first acceptance than to be in Grooms's shoes, trying to reinforce and defend your position.

Oates says the worst situation is certainly not Grooms's position since he can take ten years to write his next book and do so on a remote estate in India or Italy or wherever and live well and every once in a while transmit essays to *The New Yorker* or *Harper's* or publish excerpts of his work in progress wherever he'd like. The worst position is to have secured a good agent, achieved the goal of publication, published a few books even with esteemed publishers, and not yet feel like your career has launched, feeling in fact like it's all been a terrible mistake and your agent has sullied her reputation thanks to novels you had hopes for until you saw those hopes dashed on the rocks of a bad grade from *Entertainment Weekly*, an off-hand dismissal in *The New York Times Book Review*, a handful of two- and three-star reviews on Amazon and Goodreads, no in-depth critical review in a well-regarded outpost, nothing really from which to extract quotes for the back of the paperback, no sales of foreign rights and of course no option to make the book into a movie or series, and then when you write your third book there's more pressure than ever to write something that sells since it's not like your literary novel that didn't get any good reviews sold well, so to recoup their investment everything rides on your third book, which might not even be published by anyone, not even a small press, since your career has a stink to it: no sales, no positive reviews, unanimous dismissal of everything you've worked on and cared about for most of your adult life, but then it's not like you're going to do something else, you're not going to go into marketing or sales or learn how to code.

This is it, my friends, Oates says, this is what I do and what I will do, I'm a lifer, but there's a mouth to feed, there's college in fifteen years, a lot riding on the next thing and of course I respond to that pressure by writing an unconventional Southern Californian sprawl about violent teens that no one would ever want to read, a lightweight sensationalist mega-homage to Sims Street Wheels and those first wide Powell Peralta decks that my agent took eight months with before saying there's no way she'd represent it since it didn't seem finished, the writing was uneven, she said, like I'd glossed half of it, a third of it, and left the rest unedited, but also there was no warmth or humor or sunshine, it was all one note, once the characters were established it became a cartoon, all *POW* and *OOOPH*, violent confrontations but nothing else, *Lord of the Flies* meets *American Psycho* meets *Less Than Zero*, she said, a violent nihilistic hybrid without adding anything new, a formula she didn't think I'd solved, she said, an unsolved formula she wasn't about to try to sell. So I thanked her for saving me the embarrassment, of course, and then she gave me advice on revising the novel so it read more like a conventional crime novel. Now she wants me to write a quasi-literary crime novel set in the same time and place since she liked the setting. So now to save my career instead of fulfilling my initial ambition I'm tearing it down and starting over, ditching years of consistent work to write a quasi-literary crime novel that if it doesn't work out, if it's not published or if it's panned, means the end of my professional writing career. I'll still be able to write reviews and teach but there's no way I'll publish another novel in New York for a decade, and by then my little glowworm at home will be a butterfly expecting tuition for college that will cost several times more a year than I'll have made in my life. So that's the worst situation to be in. You guys are still striving to *not* get any sales and *not* get any reviews and have an agent you don't even work with yet turn on you. You guys would love to be in my position but I would love to be in your position, striving and hoping and starting over each time a novel's rejected by everyone, still having hopes for some semblance of success. You guys see the future as a place where you'll publish novels and I see the future as a place where *I used to* publish novels but can't manage to write a page without feeling like my skeleton's soaked and heavy, you know what I mean?

Tales of woe that Snare and England or I might tell don't seem as bad as what Oates's going through. I'd heard some of what he said before in confidence in recent months and now that he's openly proclaiming this as the most successful youngish writer in the world comes to sit with us makes me worried that a competitive streak in Oates might emerge with several more drinks, the fiery redheadedness might live up to its stereotype before too long, especially once Grooms arrives and all Oates sees is Grooms's insistence with his writer friend, like that's all Grooms has to live for at this point, all he has left to achieve, other than the Nobel Prize, whereas we all still have much simpler hopes or if our hopes have been dashed we at least haven't yet given up. Some of us may have so-called Masters degrees and have sold stories to respectable academic literary journals for a little over a hundred dollars each (plus two complimentary contributor print copies), but we're all still amateurs striving to achieve what we set out to achieve regardless of how agents and editors respond to our writing. Agents and editors represent the market and the market can't dictate the degree to which we follow our passions, the degree to which we pursue our goals.

We are professional amateurs, ultimately, *expert amateurs*, except for Oates who's a professional and therefore claims he's in a worse position. It's apparently much better to be an expert amateur, never a master or a professional, a self-loathing player of a loathsome game, but then right as we order another round of drinks as though to wash away Oates's revelation (I order an India Pale Ale this time, wanting something stronger), Gibson begins to speak and we realize that when the server returns we must with extreme urgency order a round of shots.

XVI.

Gibson solemnly thumps his drained pint glass on the table, calling our court to order, and begins to speak in such a way that makes us bow our heads. We sense this is the big one, the earthquake that leaves the city in ruins, so we stare into our drinks and listen.

When I first met Gibson he said something I had never heard another writer say. He said it as though it were something all writers, especially *expert amateur* writers, always think. Instead of thinking about what we're reading and writing, about writers and their writing, about wanting to write when not writing, about wanting to read when not reading, about wanting to quit jobs to live in a hovel in some far-flung land where we can write every day, every hour, always writing, not to mention live a unique un-American life, Gibson said something like of course the question we all ask ourselves is should we quit, or when are we going to quit, or isn't it about time we quit? Something along these lines Gibson once said to me as though it were matter of fact, as though it hovered over all of us, as though the question of quitting was the ultimate question at this point.

All our backs are to the wall and the wall has long sharp spikes coming out of it and some monstrous embodiment of Defeat is coming toward us. There's no escape other than to wake from the dream before we're impaled or consumed. The choice for Gibson: either be impaled on spikes or consumed by some monstrous embodiment of failed ambitions.

I've never thought anything like this. I've never once thought about quitting writing. I've quit so many things and considered it a natural evolution but I've never once thought about *quitting writing.* I've quit jobs more often than not so I could read and write without obstacles. I've always quit in the name of writing, so there's never a sense that I would one day quit writing.

Quitting writing would kill off what most brought the world to life. It would kill the part of me I've cultivated to take over the entire person. I consider myself more of a reader than a writer but I really only read to absorb and experience and express at some later date once it comes through me as I write. I read the way I do because I write the way I do. I write the way I do because I read the way I do. If I had to choose reading over writing I would talk myself into believing that reading was preparation for writing once the hypothetical ban on writing were lifted. But if I had to quit both writing and reading I would work in some field unrelated to reading and writing, dedicate myself to it and work on it 24/7/365, the time I now spend on my full-time office-based editorial job and extracurricular reading and writing. Quitting reading and writing would leave me with only my job, without an organizing principle for my time on earth, which is why I didn't understand when I first met Gibson and he said the question we all ask ourselves is *should we quit?* or *when are we going to quit?* or *isn't it about time we quit and devoted ourselves to improving the lives of our families?*

Gibson had an infant at the time when he first mentioned quitting writing and now a few years later after much work and no reward, he calls our little court to order, to attention, with a thump of his pint on the table and then he bows his head and issues what seems, conveyed by the loquacious clarity of the first few rounds, like an official provision of notice regarding his intent to cease all production for the foreseeable future, although he says it more like:

Guys, you all know this is something I've been thinking about for a while, it's something I've mentioned before, it's something Throop brings up every time he's had three beers, it's something I've been telegraphing for years now and so I figured today I would announce what I've known for a while and what I've discussed with Casey ad nauseum, she's literally *nauseated* by it, sick of the whole discussion that's taken maybe a year or two from both our lives, which is a really long time to talk about the benefits and drawbacks of quitting writing, and so we've decided, Casey and I, that the best thing for me, for us, is to stop talking about quitting writing, never talk about it again, and the only way I can stop obsessive thoughts about quitting writing is to, finally, today, tonight, on this Bloomsday, the only way I can stop thinking and talking about quitting writing is to hereby announce my intention, once and for all and finally and for good, to quit writing so I can stop talking about quitting writing and get on with my life and start talking about something that has some value for anyone other than myself.

That's the thing about all the work for no reward that goes into it, Gibson says, there's so much effort and if that effort, if that *time*, were spent on anything of value for anyone in need or anything other than so-called art it would be so much better for everyone. I've loved writing in the past but I've loved it mostly in the past. It's not something that brings me pleasure in the present because all the time I'm wondering why I'm spending all this time on it when I should be spending time with my kid or my wife or spending time making more money or whatever but instead I'm devoting so many wasted hours a week to working on writing that no one will ever care about, and so I think the writing has been on the wall for a while about quitting writing, and now it's time to stop what's been driving me and everyone around me a bit mad the past few years. Again it's not that I think you guys should quit too, it's just that I can't see spending so much time writing and more so *talking* about quitting writing when I should be doing something, anything, else. Nothing is worse than talking all the time about quitting something you used to love, but also there's been a feeling recently knowing I was going to announce this tonight, there's been a feeling recently of alleviation, weight off my shoulders, and so I would like to toast *not* to quitting writing but to the alleviation that comes from making a decision to do something, even if the something I've decided to do involves *not doing* something you all deem essential to your existence.

Gibson raises a refreshed full pint and we all raise our glasses and he says *to alleviation* and we clink and take deep sips and observe an impossible-to-imagine second or two of silence, since we're always talking, always staining the silence, but now after Gibson vows to extend his writing silence indefinitely we're silenced for a second until Snare breaks it and says *whew.* He says it loud enough and with enough comic effect that we all laugh, relieved he's alleviated the burden we felt once we toasted *alleviation* regarding a decision to quit writing.

England says *jeez* I hope these thoughts about quitting writing aren't contagious, and then he covers mouth with forearm.

We reach for a way to break the silence after this official announcement of a decision to quit writing so he can stop talking with his wife and his child who is now maybe four or five and probably asks him to read what he's writing and then most likely offers critiques only a toddler can hurl at her father's writing, never once thinking about positive reinforcement, considering the father's writing competition for his attention and affection.

The wave of post-announcement responses flows my way from Snare to England so I clear my throat and enunciate as clearly as possible and raise my voice but don't necessarily yell, I simply say *that's bullshit, Gibson,* total bullshit, especially today of all days, on Bloomsday, our one true holy day.

Everyone smiles since I smile as I say it but I'm not sure I'm joking. I've reached the point in the night where I speak from both sides of my mouth. I haven't said much since showing up. I've sat here and listened even if I've heard it all before. I've heard everything Snare and England have to say. I've heard bits of Oates's story about rewriting *Death by Jacaranda* into something more commercial called *California Über Alles*. I've heard Gibson muse about quitting writing but never have I heard him take the next step. This is something new, a milestone in the history of our time together as writer reader drinker friends. This has a chance to skew the status quo.

Would Gibson still drink with us if he doesn't have anything to add about his writing?

Will we ask how's your *not* writing going?

Got a lot more free time to play with the kid?

How's Casey enjoying *not* hearing you talk about writing, or hearing you talk about how happy you are *not* to be writing?

Do you think you'll be happier just because you've stopped writing?

Don't you think you started writing because you were unhappy?

Don't you think that unhappiness is the foundation and has nothing to do with whether or not you write?

I don't ask these questions but they all form at once. There would be nothing finer than to divulge everything in one propulsive mess, a cleansing purge of every thought about writing and every beer drank while talking with writer reader drinker friends. I don't feel queasy, however; more so, semi-restored thanks to what Gibson said. Soreness thanks to the long walking-and-reading session seems to have eased. Worries about wife on couch seem eased. Concerns about production and publication of my own writing seem eased now that a colleague has packed it in.

Calling bullshit on Gibson's announcement makes me feel better about my own writing. I do it and I will do it and I won't stop, it's not an issue for me, has never been an issue. I've never considered *quitting writing* because it takes time from other aspects of life. It's not a concern because it's not a question. Reading and writing are substantial and satisfying on a significant level, to say a religious level doesn't sound like an exaggeration. The weight of the books on our bookshelves, the beauty of their spines, the pattern of all those rectangular verticals insulating the wall, the weight and beauty and depth of the books, each containing tens of thousands, hundreds of thousands of words about life, I can't imagine not wanting to contribute to that weight and beauty and depth, that heft and truth. I can't imagine thinking it's not worth the effort. I can't imagine thinking I'd be better off doing anything other than writing, than thinking and talking about writing, than reading as a way to talk to writers long gone before me.

I also call bullshit on Gibson's announcement because I'm protecting the homeland, punishing recalcitrance, this attempt by the oldest among us (not in terms of age) to break rank.

We are literary fundamentalists, after all, and we won't stand for a fellow soldier to proclaim a desire to return to civilian life before the battle ends, or really even before it begins.

I love the word *battle*, the India Pale Ale energizing me, the higher alcohol content, the spiciness, the syrupy sweetness, like a blend of honey and translucent oil. It accesses the hefeweizens and charges them with purpose. What had been almost a soporific, an analgesic, transforms into an invigorator, a tonic.

We're rustled by Gibson's announcement. We aren't alleviated so much as released. Our circuitry was set and now we stir to life.

It's not bullshit, says Gibson. I apologize for besmirching your beloved Bloomsday, holiest of holy days, I mean no disrespect, but it's not *bullshit*, as you so elegantly put it Mr. Roebling. It's necessary, something I have to do to keep things right at home. Don't take this the wrong way but I spend more time with wife and daughter than I do with any of you, not that you guys and all this isn't important to me. I could say I write and sit with you guys and ask questions about how the writing's going, could say it's going pretty well or not so hot or anything at all, could shake my head and say I'd really rather not talk about it tonight but how's your stuff coming, Kev? How's your stuff, John? What about you, Throop? Honestly, for the most part, other than intermittent minor progress over the past year, that's exactly what I've been doing, hiding behind smoke screens, asking questions the way I grilled Mr. Snare tonight. The best defense is a good offense. I'm good at asking questions because that's what I've done to myself for years. I need to know the answers in advance before I advance my manuscript. It's not bullshit. It's tiring thankless work and we all know my time could be better spent.

Everyone looks at me to address his rebuttal.

No, I say, I disagree with everything you're saying, every last word is total and utter bullshit. I smile as I speak and Gibson and Oates at least, the two across from me, smile too, reflecting my smile. I find it totally untenable, I say, that one among us would quit, would stop at the crucial moment, *the crucial moment*, right before we join forces with someone like Grooms. You undermine our unity with this announcement regarding your intention to quit. Listen up, you can check out any time you want but you can never leave. Writing is a life sport. You can't just quit. Your brain has been altered by chronic exposure to thoughts about writing, to sitting down for hours at a time by yourself writing. Most people don't sit down for hours at a time and write in their lives. They write emails or social media posts now the way they used to write letters but for the most part in one week we all spend more time sitting and writing than most extended families do in all their lives. In one week we do more battle with language and ambition and imagination than most do in their lives. You're a veteran of those battles, Mr. Gibson. You can't quit being a veteran. A war veteran can't quit being a war veteran. You can't just stop thinking about the battles you've been through. You've been through countless soul battles with the world and yourself and you've left behind a trail of words. You can't say it didn't happen, can't announce on *Bloomsday* of all days, right before Holy Moly

Freaking Goddamn *Jonathan David Grooms* appears, that you're pack-
ing it in and everything you've been through on the page and in your
head and talked about et cetera mean nothing. You can't quit what's
inside you. So I'm calling bullshit because whether or not you're a
writer isn't your decision and it's not my decision. The decision has
been made by chronic exposure to writing and the related periph-
erals. You're infected, buddy, irradiated, glowing bright green with
it.

It's clear my friends, my comrades, my fellow literary fundamentalists at the enormous Viking vessel booth are becoming a bit restless so I shut it down and slap England's strong round shoulder as
though tagging him next to weigh in.

XVII.

England, as expected, says that he doesn't know what's so wrong with wanting to quit. I don't know, he says, if he wants to quit for a while let him quit, it's not like anyone cares, the world will not come to a halt, even if Jonathan David Grooms himself stops writing or publishing, the world will go on. I mean, I don't know, he's only going to live once so why should he spend his one life worrying about writing, talking to his wife about it? It's better to try to change what's giving him a hard time.

Rimbaud quit, says Oates, who else? The idea that it's an important act is overstated, I'd say, says Oates, addressing me, his nostril's peachy pink lobes flaring as though their movement fans his thoughts, how a manta ray propels itself through water with the gentle, respiration-like undulation of its wings. Oates says the publishing industry has been vaporized by technological progress and post-literate entertainment so the chances of publishing anything are slim to none. Only a few lucky ones are damned to see their stuff make it into print and be torn apart by critics online and lax sales. It's much better to write your own private literature. Even better to only contribute to a *potential literature*, a fictional literature. It's becoming clear that a literature in print is an artifact of a by-gone century, my friends. The future of literature is a potential literature, Oates says, a literature no one bothers to read or even bothers to write, a figment of the imagination, an imaginary literature only in the minds of those who'd only write if it were worth the time it took to write on the level of canonical excellence. Spending all that time to write at a level other than canonical excellence doesn't make sense because there are so many good things to watch. Never before in the history of human existence have writers had to compete with so many sources of narrative entertainment, even the news, the way it unfolds first as tweets and then as hastily written headlines from wire services and then headlines and stories before it's spoofed on comedy shows. The minute-by-minute refreshing of new developments is a new narrative entertainment, always on auto refresh, status updates emerging, vying for a moment of attention before they're replaced and replaced and replaced et cetera by what comes next, a customized improvised collage of updates, links, photographs, commentary, criticism, affirmation, argument, promotion, propaganda, propagation, one long page that scrolls ineluctably into the past, beating on forever although really only until the mid-2000s. Information archaeologists will mine the archives, that will be someone's fulltime job, that will be the fulltime job of everyone in the department of information archaeology at every major institution of higher learning in the world. If born today in thirty years we could all be information archaeologists, but we were not born today, Oates says, or yesterday. Our friend Gibson here wants to be *reborn today* as a civilian, he wants to give up the fight, and that's his right, Oates says, he has every right not to fight it if it's not a fight he feels like he can win. We all want to run up the white flag sometimes, we all do it some days, so imagine if that's what it feels like every time you sit down to write. All you see is that white flag and you want to raise it and stop trying to concentrate on what you're working on. If you can't concentrate on what you're working on you can't work at all, it's impossible to fight the fight if instead of concentrating on what you're writing you're distracted by the idea of no longer being obligated to sit and concentrate. It's much better to spend your life doing something else than forcing yourself to do something you don't want to do when you can't do it without so much effort it taxes you and you're unhappy and dissatisfied with the results, Oates says. If you were happy with the results it would be a different thing, it would be worth it to tax yourself for satisfactory pages, but if you produce not much and what you produce isn't up to your standards, it's best to announce your intention to take some extended rest and recuperation time. But Throop's right, Oates says, you can't really quit it, the brain circuitry's damaged by all the reading and writing and thinking and perceiving and channeling everything into what you're working on when you're in deep concentration mode, deeply imagining what doesn't exist based on what most certainly does, but that doesn't mean you can't proclaim yourself reborn on this the one hundred and eighth anniversary of the day Stephen Dedalus and Leopold Bloom wandered around Dublin and crossed paths out on the town that night in a pub or a brothel, Oates says.

Snare says that in the year since the last Bloomsday celebration he hasn't fulfilled his vow to have read *Ulysses* by the time the next Bloomsday rolls around. England claims to have read it a long time ago and seems familiar with the major characters and structure, as though he read about it online. Gibson has read it and has been to Dublin, Snare has been to Dublin too, England may have been too, Oates too. I have never been and really have no more interest in Dublin. I'm more interested in central European capitals flourishing now well after the fall of Communism, Zagreb, Vilnius, Ljubljana, not that I think about these places much, but they seem more attractive than Dublin, not that I will go anywhere in the next several years thanks to the baby. At most we'll take a hiking trip when the kid can walk well enough, a trip to Washington DC, not sure if I'll ever see the world the way I once thought I'd see it.

I had once been so restless, pacing floors and swiping my fingers against the ceiling, had been ready to travel and write like Joyce the itinerant teacher of English as a second language in Trieste. I once thought I'd travel around the world as cheaply as possible, see ev-

erything, and write about everything I saw, but restlessness and desire to see everything and write about it gave way to a desire to stay
put and accumulate books and read as much as I could and do my
best to write what I could and live where I lived without worrying
too much about the infinite possibilities of other lives, other places
to live, other people one might live with, other areas of the country,
other countries. All the permutations of people and places are more
than enough to undermine the ability to concentrate, which, more
than anything else, is a prerequisite for reading and writing, more
for writing than for reading but also required for reading.

I'm sure Gibson wants to move to Dublin and sit in a little rented
room lit at most by a lantern or yellowed lampshade and sit at a simple desk and immerse himself in what he's writing. I'm sure he wants
at times to make the drastic irresponsible move and flee his family
in the name of fulfilling his ambition. It's not that at home he can't
write, he can find a quiet hour when everyone's asleep, he can slip
out to a café for half an hour and get half a page down a day, he
can work with his family to let him have a set time to write, a protected time, but even then his family is on his mind. Instead of seeing into the world he's writing, thoughts turn toward family, discus-
sions with wife about daughter, he can't just turn it on, he needs
more time to settle into it, to fall into the dream in which he's no
longer aware he's at his keyboard describing what he sees, although
he's never been that sort of writer. I can't impose my processes on
him. He's a more premeditative writer, a willful writer, someone
conscious of effects, motivations, pressure on characters intended to
force action with consequences the character then must face. Writing is a battle for Gibson more than it is for me, so why submit to
battle if it goes nowhere, if he produces pages and lays them next to
the pages of writing he loves and sees that what he loves compares
favorably, without a doubt.

It had been such a beautiful day but now the weather in the room seems dreary. England says he doesn't know but he thinks maybe it's fine to quit for a while to do something else so you can start again when the spirit moves you, make a fresh start. It's premature to say you're quitting for good since people often come back from retirement, especially if they retire early. The only time you won't come back to it is when you can't come back to it, when you're dead or something, England says, and there's no denying it.

Gibson appreciates the sentiment that the end he's declared isn't necessarily the end, it may just be the end for now, that after a time he'll rise again. It's clear he's put too much pressure on himself. Two years in Iowa City created expectations that he would publish soon after the Workshop and since he's increased the pressure on himself to publish to the point that there's no way he can even continue writing, let alone complete something worthy of publication. In short, the only way for Gibson to write something he can publish is to quit writing.

It makes perfect sense to me and so I say it aloud: the only way to write something publishable is to quit writing.

I say it like a proclamation of deep truth. I raise my glass and clink it with everyone. It's absurd on the surface yet clear to me that quitting writing means quitting Writing with a capital W like that, quitting Writing that adheres to conventions and expectations, especially the conventions and expectations of the market.

The only way to write something publishable, Oates says, is to forget about trying to write something publishable by conventional publishers. The only way to write something worthwhile for oneself and others is to quit writing for unknown agents and unknown editors in Manhattan between Central Park and Canal. There's more to the world than literary professionals in Manhattan between Central Park and Canal. The idea isn't to supply the market with product but to create a product of the imagination intended for readers. If you focus on readers and your own necessities it won't matter how unknown agents and editors respond to your work, even if they respond favorably and agree to represent you and agree to purchase and promote your manuscript and all your work pays off and your work is promoted and reviewed and sold for a time, only to disappear soon enough, remaindered, available for a few dollars in the discount bins at The Strand until your books disappear from everywhere other than the used listings on Amazon, available for a penny plus shipping.

Oates says let's not forget: none of it matters and no one cares. I don't mean that nihilistically, he says. If you don't want to write, if you don't feel moved to write, the world won't end, but if you do it out of necessity or even out of habit at this point the way I do, you can't think too much about it, you do what you can do.

Snare says athletes always say they can only control what they can control and whenever they're cut or released or traded they say they understand the organization had to make a business decision and go in another direction, but still we got in this game to control the world in a way, right? Snare says we started writing to control the world around us and so when it's time to share the world you've controlled so well it's not a pleasant feeling when your world is deemed undesirable and everything wonderful and alive about the world you worked so hard to create and control, all its active living details, are warped by rejection and when you look at it again you see it through the lens of rejection, you talk shit about it to friends, downplay it, say there're parts I like but all in all it's a failure. You say this, Snare says, about something that months ago you loved, months ago you had every line memorized, months earlier you sent queries to agents like you were sending a gift, like you were doing them a favor by choosing them to represent you among all the possible literary agents in Manhattan between Central Park and Canal Street, as Oates said, you chose this agent to represent your work and bestowed your novel upon a good agent in New York and they responded soon after that they were interested in reading it and could you please either email it as an attachment to their assistant or send a printout marked "requested materials" on the envelope, and you send it off and expect overjoyed responses to flow into your life days later, once the agent starts reading. You suspect you're not crazy and what you think is good in your own writing will also be thought good by the agent and they will clamor for you to work with them, they will include the word "please" in their response to your manuscript, they will say they've already forwarded the attachment to editors who might be interested. That's how easy it is these days, sharing among friends. Within a few weeks options will be presented, an auction date, a bid beyond anything the agent expected, a contract including another unwritten novel, a job essentially handed to you, the future set. Sure, there will be pressure on the back end of the two-book deal, but all hopes are fulfilled, all dreams are becoming reality. Sure, there'll be disappointments later on but for now the goal has been accomplished, to write and sell a novel to a major New York City publisher, to feel what it's like for a day or two to feel what it's like to be Jonathan David Grooms every day, Snare says as he looks toward the door, which does not open with Lao Guardian leading the way followed by Jonathan David Grooms in dark aviator-style sunglasses and a silvery sparkly cape, Jonathan David Grooms in top hat and tuxedo, the iconic author photo of Jonathan David Grooms taken by Marion Ettlinger, a blast of dry-ice fog through which Jonathan David Grooms skates in wearing a silvery sparkly leotard, flourishing his arms like scepters more than body parts, twirling into the dark loud bar in such a way that sends a magnetic shock toward the jukebox so Motörhead cuts off in favor of Boston's "More Than A Feeling," Lao Guardian high-stepping with an open-mouthed smile, presenting the great writer, who shakes our hands wearing white gloves and on our palms leaves behind a pixie dust-like residue, a little gift best collected and preserved for display at one's home.

As Snare seems progressively angry about how everyone's hopes are dashed upon the rocks of literary rejection, I imagine Jonathan David Grooms sitting down with us maybe within the hour, Harry Houdini crossed with a younger version of Fagin from *Oliver Twist*, maybe some young Gandalf in there too. There's something diabolical and attractive about him, thanks in part to monocle and cape and white gloved hands laced with a dust that when sniffed seems to energize everyone and intensify conversations, everyone talking at once until Lao stands and inserts index fingers into sides of mouth and emits a conversation-ceasing whistle. Lao then says listen up guys, Jonathan David Grooms here, he's asked me to let you know he's nice enough to grant y'all one wish each, but don't be stupid about it, it's not a magic wish like you wish you could fly, make it a reasonable wish like publication in *The New Yorker*, that sort of thing, think careerist wish fulfillment, OK guys?

Lao settles in and as we one by one whisper our wishes into Grooms's ear and he nods and smiles and says, with confidence and humility, consider it done, my friend, consider it done. One by one he listens and nods and says consider it done. I wonder what we're all wishing for although I'm sure I'll find out soon enough. I can't even think about what I'd wish for since I can only picture Grooms and Lao and Oates and Gibson and England and Snare leaning their heads together across the table the best they can, whispering, nodding, conspiring about a future of success based on this moment of wishes and promises to fulfill them.

Conspiring etymologically means coming together to breathe, they're all breathing together, there's something diabolical about the image of them breathing together, a witch's Sabbath, Grooms the goat-headed devil and my writer friends with distorted soot-smudged peasant faces. Maybe I want to protect myself from it, I want to keep myself out of it the way at first when invited to attend this special installment of our annual Bloomsday celebration a strong majority in me voiced its resentment about having to come. That was my real first reaction after the initial positive response, my first real intuitive response was stay home and work. I didn't want to achieve a semblance of success based on a nod and smile and snapping of gloved fingers dusted with magic cocaine, and now when I think of what to ask him, what wish to make his command, it doesn't involve literary achievement.

I want to make sure my super-pregnant wife at home on the couch and the baby she carries make it through the remaining in utero time without complication and the kid is born healthy and has every chance to grow up without having to fight upstream through too serious a malady, too serious a medical condition that holds him back from doing whatever it is he'll want to do. I want to ask my imaginary diabolical genie version of Jonathan David Grooms to grant me a wish that bestows health upon my unborn son forever, also ensuring if possible the perinatal health of my wife, also bestowing if possible upon me the energy and flexibility to provide for him, and then maybe bestowing upon me persistence of what I already seem to possess in terms of writing, the gift of writing because it organizes my life, of writing because it's what I do, of writing because it's how I live my life, of writing because it's how I concentrate, of writing because I love unfurling unruly expanses of language I thereafter order, of writing because I love the dream of connecting with unknown readers whose shapes I intuit pressing through the page or the off-white screen, the chins and noses and brows and foreheads of unknown readers pressing their faces against a bedsheet separating us, not just as writer and reader but across time. I imagine my son reading my writing after I'm gone. I imagine grandchildren reading my writing after I'm gone. There's no way of knowing how it will live in the world once it's written, New York isn't the only entrance, or maybe in twenty years I'll write something that catches the eye of an influential agent and everything else will be published based on that success, a storehouse of writing once thought unpublishable released upon as many readers as possible.

I have no way of knowing what the future holds for what I write, I have no control of it, but I can influence the future of my child, I think, I can help him along, the way I can help my writing along, nurture it, make sure I don't do anything to raise it up in such a way that hampers it from the start. That's a wish granted right there. I imagine a genie writer granting literary wishes and I reject the offer and assure myself of my ability to raise the child.

Once upon a time I had thought they were similar, the unborn child in my wife and the novel I worked on each morning. I'd started the novel around the time she conceived in the early fall, when it was still warm. I remember bare feet and shorts when I wrote outside in the little back patio area enclosed by a tall wooden fence streaming with blue and pink morning glory flowers opening as the sun climbed the vines. I wrote by hand, coffee nearby, unbuttoned long sleeve shirt over T-shirt I'd slept in, wife interrupting one morning soon after I'd started something new saying she thought she might be pregnant. From then on it's been a suspended time as she rounds out toward the July 7 due date, less than a month from Bloomsday, three weeks or so.

At first we started calling the due date *the dude date.* We started dreaming of a boy although we both wanted to wait to find out so we wouldn't be flooded with gendered baby clothes before the kid had a chance to clear its first breath. We were adamant about not wanting to know the sex but we thought it was a boy, referred to the fetus as a he, and *he* became a habit. I asked how *he* was doing, not she. I said *he's* looking good. It's not that we wanted a boy more than a girl, it's that we started dreaming of his high school sports career, waking early and instead of writing going to the park to shoot hoops, running him around the three-point line perimeter, feeding him passes, rebounding for the kid. We would watch sports together and communicate via commentary on games, players, statistics, scores, records. I wanted to share that experience with him. I envision a scrappy seven-year-old boy a year removed from Little League, knees of jeans torn from infield practice, from sliding in soccer games, from tackle football. I see myself at that age, I realize, and he will be someone other than me. Reproduction isn't replication. He will be a different person, at times an enemy, demanding attention at a pivotal moment in my writing career. Nonexistent writing career in terms of conventional indicators of achievement will remain nonexistent because I can't achieve anything, unable to concentrate, unable to write for a living when not at work. Life will be too complicated to nurture a writing child stitched together with filaments of language, who rarely stands and casts a shadow, same as my wife all the time on the couch these days.

A month from the dude date I would limit my alcohol intake, I'd said, no more than two beers any given night. I would be on call, ready to shuttle her to the birthing suite ten blocks north from our house. She has a bag packed and ready to go. We've taken classes. She's read everything available, scoured every horror story for traces of symptoms she's experienced. All that's left is for the little guy to emerge. But early in the evening when I downed two quick glasses of wine before I left I decided we would not be engaged in birthing activities tonight. No precursor tremors, nothing more than regular jerks and hiccups and dancing inside her. Some heartburn, sure, but that was expected late in the third trimester.

Wife on the couch hugely pregnant.

Writer friends at the bar trying to bring novels into the world.

It's not like every night I'm out sitting at this enormous booth. Lately I've been home on the couch most nights, typing and editing what I wrote in the morning, sprinting to finish a draft of another unpublishable novel before the baby arrives. I have in fact turned down invitations to leave the house in recent weeks. I've stayed in as days lengthened and Lao or England text from tables outside this same bar, sun setting later, pints a-glow in the angled light. I would never experience it the same way. Child would always be in back of mind as I enjoy life without him, trying to experience again what had once been available whenever I wanted it depending on availability of seating, companions, sweetness of weather. Certain goblets of ale held to the setting sun in early summer are worth the higher price. But this is Bloomsday, can't stay inside with wife and unborn child and watch over her and work, can't restrain desire for one last hurrah, one last significant evening, especially when capped by the arrival of a famous writer genie devil granting wishes all around.

XVIII.

The sun has absolutely set. No sign of Lao or Grooms. It's remarkable how little we've played on our phones but bringing out my phone to check the time (past nine) causes Oates to bring his phone out and it cascades around the table. Conversation becomes distracted as everyone peers into their little worlds for updates. I stand and excuse myself. In the bathroom I hold my phone over the toilet as I pursue the news for no good reason. A woman drove her car into a crowded town square in Ohio, injuring two dozen, some pinned under the car until bystanders lifted it. I should drop my phone in the toilet, the bathroom like a scary little cabin in the woods where bad kids do unsavory things, like that but smaller, rotting, the wood of the walls exposed to excessive humidity in the form of urine on the floor.

Back out in open air the barroom seems pristine, the air fresh in comparison. I slip outside and, relatively free of hassle, bum a cigarette. I lean against an old trolley pole fifteen feet from the corner entrance and from there can see everyone eating at tables along one sidewalk heading east and an unimpeded view of pedestrian traffic down the other sidewalk proceeding southwest. It's a good place to stand, the street corner like an arrowhead of cement. I stand with my back to our version of the castle on the hill. Skyscrapers for the cable TV/internet company, for banks, no idea what else. I text wife and request update regarding status on couch. I otherwise let the air hold me up. I respire through the pores of my skin, the cigarette an excuse to stand outside and hold an ember in my hand. I only take a drag or two, wanting to inhale new summer air more than smoke. Every inhalation elevates everything for a second and then drops it back in place.

What a world, I think, but also I sense low-level tremor, the sort of feeling I get before a reading, before a meeting at work where I'll present something I've worked on for a while, wholly human I think, not requiring medication, not pathological. Everything about not wanting an evil genie version of Grooms to grant me a wish is off. My body tells me so. He won't help us all, might not help any of us. He'll respond to questions as he fusses with his phone, steps outside to make a call that lasts most of the time he's here. Snare will attack him about the novel he's pounded with his fist all night. Snare will infuriate Grooms, who from high above will drop a devastating *bon mot* upon Snare's head and leave insulted as Lao runs after him. Not knowing what will happen causes low-level tremor. Snare was right about controlling what we do, and then having no control. The more I control worlds in writing the less I endure the uncontrollable world.

My wife described it as playing dolls, how she and her sister played dolls and moved them around and made them talk and get in little fights. You do it too, she said, except you're grown men playing with language for a so-called reader, however you dress your dolls up, she said. All the talk about point of view, plot and character dynamics, setting, dialogue, the art of exaggeration, it's only to make it seem like you aren't *playing dolls*, animating inanimate humanoids with projections of language. All the shop talk, she said, legitimizes what's essentially *playing dolls* in your imagination and leaving behind a trail of language. *Playing dolls* in language, she said, and I laughed, happy to have married a woman who makes fun of what we do.

In college and a year after college she'd written stories and sent them out without success and so stopped sending out stories and stopped writing new stories, letting her writing instinct emerge through email, blog posts, updates, comments, tweets. She'd blogged for a while instead of writing stories, but her blog had been down for years, since before we'd met. I'm sure it was good. I married a funny intelligent woman who will soon be the mother of my child. We'll gather on the floor and play some variety of dolls at some point. I'm sure I'll be not so hot at it. The circuitry of my brain only plays dolls with silent written language, and yet by all accounts the trails I leave behind aren't up to snuff.

The in-laws are not impressed I spend so much time on writing that's not published.

Why don't I try to publish stories in *The New Yorker*, they ask.

I say it's not like I write stories intended for publication in *The New Yorker*.

They say but that's something a writer could shoot for, publication in *The New Yorker*.

Holy grail for ten million writers, I say. But I no longer even read *The New Yorker*.

Grooms has a "right of first refusal" contract with them. They pay more than other places as long as Grooms agrees to send his work to them first. That's the goal of most writers on earth, to sign a right of first refusal contract with *The New Yorker*. I don't feel like a writer on earth, however. But what if Grooms tells me to call his editor at *The New Yorker*? What if on Lao's recommendation alone he recommends me to his editor at *The New Yorker*?

Standing on the tip of a concrete arrowhead facing the city's skyscrapers, finishing off a cigarette I've hardly smoked, it seems these thoughts emerge from low-level tremor about having a child. To some degree I want to achieve success at the level of publication in *The New Yorker*. All I have to do is study stories by Richard Yates, John Cheever, Alice Munro, E.L. Doctorow, William Maxwell, do my best to imitate and update them, *internationalize* them if possible, work on a few stories for as long as I work on a novel and send them one by one to *The New Yorker*, to agents, to the best possible alternatives to *The New Yorker* when *The New Yorker* responds with kind and encouraging form-letter rejections, hope for a personal response, wait months for the possibility of a personal response from *The New Yorker* while writing better stories, undeniable stories. The alternative is to publish individuated novels with small presses until *The New Yorker* solicits excerpts or stories or essays. Sounds like a plan. *Uh-huh. Sure.*

I toss the cigarette into the gutter and when I look back toward the skyscrapers I see Lao and Grooms. I recognize Lao's jerky walk and blond hair, it's clearly him walking with a taller, athletic man with kinky brown hair, almost like an afro, short on the sides, taller on top, rising off a high brow, maybe a receding hairline, not wearing the black-framed writer glasses he'd popularized in his first author photo, well before Franzen's headshot in *The Corrections*. Grooms walks comparatively steadily, gracefully, wears what looks like a long white linen shirt, black knee-length shorts, and even at a distance under streetlights I can see he wears black athletic socks pulled mid-calf and sneakers of some sort.

I lean against the light pole, my back to the skyscrapers and Lao and Grooms's approach, my head craned around to watch them come, sort of hiding, not running toward them or jumping up and down shouting *you're here, you're here, you're finally here*. They don't see me. Lao jerks his arms now and again as he talks. Grooms has his hands in his pockets, stoops a little, nods, laughs, enjoying Lao's animated proclamations. People eating and drinking at tables outside have no idea that Jonathan David Grooms is a block away, but then again I have no idea how many of these people have read him. We assume he's a household name but we also understand it's possible no one knows him. He has never been on Oprah, has never been on the cover of *Time*, his books have become movies but never specifically promoted as "based on a Jonathan David Grooms novel," in fact I rarely see people reading his books whenever I see someone reading at a bar or café or a park. Reading in public isn't a common sight in this city, in part why I walk and read, to advertise the existence of old-fashioned physical books but also the old-fashioned existence of the act of reading. The crowd eating and drinking might be denigrated as hipsters, younger couples mostly, some might play in bands or they're visual artists who read Murakami at most. The city seems occupied by musicians and visual artists more than writers and readers. The city in the summertime seems filled with tattooed bicyclists but that perception may only have been based on proximity to this bar.

I run inside before Lao and Grooms see me. The front barroom area is packed. I angle my way through it, guide myself gently past people standing behind those seated at the bar to our table where it seems my seat is now occupied by two younger female writers we know, friends of ours from the neighborhood. The booth is filled almost to capacity, at most it seats six or seven if the seventh is petite, but with England, Snare, Oates, Gibson, and now with Lena and Feliz, too, there's really no room for me to sit and blend in with everyone, but the booth next to ours has two people sitting at it and we can spill over, I suppose, we'll have to, so I ask if I can sit at the edge of their booth since we're overflowing our booth and the couple next to us nods and scoots toward the barroom away from our group. I sit at this nearly empty booth as Lena and Feliz amuse everyone.

Neither Lena nor Feliz are married or in long-term relationships and they entertain Oates and Gibson, particularly, who have both been married so long that simply *talking* to a single woman is a thrill. England has stood on the verge with both Lena and Feliz but as far as anyone knows hasn't stepped over it with either. Flirtatious sparring among them has recently turned sour. Lena and Feliz have made a point of saying *England* in a way that sounds derogatory. They've turned his name into a slur they say to his face, which England seems to appreciate. There's a masochistic side to him that emerges after a few beers. Lena and Feliz see it better than anyone and go after it. England's masochistic side opens like a flower that Lena and Feliz pollinate with tender violence so the night may be remembered as a good time had by all.

Oates seems flabbergasted in a *there goes the neighborhood* way, amused with the presence of these women but also irritated since the Bloomsday ritual is a manly affair, historically. Do they know a sentence or passage to quote when it's time to recite famous lines, favorite lines, the high point of the night, shouting lines about *metempsychosis* as the bar churns toward last call? Lao probably alerted Lena to the arrival of Grooms since Lao and Lena live on the same block and Lena often sits for Lao's son. Lena's a writer more like Lao than Oates, Snare, or England, or Gibson, who no longer writes.

Lena and Feliz both have MFAs, unlike me, the only uncreden-tialled entity at the table. Lena completed the low-residency pro-gram at Bennington. Feliz had worked at The Strand and earned an MFA in poetry at The New School. After relocating to South Philly, she switched to fiction but writes fiction that reads like poetry without line breaks, deep-POV fiction, fiction microscopically zoomed in so instead of seeing a panorama of St. Petersburg in flames and thresh-ing long grass in the fields with a scythe, her stuff seems more like mi-croscopic paisley, like histological images of carcinogenic pathogens, squirmy and invisible to the naked eye. Feliz looks more like Frida Kahlo than anyone I've ever met, maybe half Sicilian or half Cuban, eyebrows prominent, skin olive, hair dark and pulled up in a bun in which she stores sharpened Ticonderoga #2 pencils, whereas Lena writes psychoerotic sensationalism, spare stories involving children, leery male relatives, some surreal element with an explicitly per-verted sexual side to it.

Lena tends to wear dark velvet gowns with heavy black leather boots. Every so often she dyes her hair a purplish black, mostly so natural blond roots can show over time, her preferred look. She either always has actual dark circles around her eyes or they're a permanent after-effect of Goth days of yore. These days, she's active in the online literary world, the way I had been active in it before I devoted time to writing novels instead of odd little stories to post on unconventional lit sites.

The online literary world peaked at first in 2002 and then fell off as the first round of unconventional little lit sites lost steam as blogging emerged and then the next wave refreshed it in 2008 or so with a group blog that attracted writers who posted strange short language-y stories on sites that streamed across the world's browsers before editors lost interest, stopped paying hosting fees, and saw their alt-lit domains replaced by advertisements for debt consolidation. Whenever Lena and I talk about the latter round of sites, most losing steam themselves recently, we talk about how the earlier sites had a sense of humor whereas the latter sites are humorless. Earlier writing online had seemed odd and perverted and *amusing* whereas later writing online seems odd and perverted and *humorless*. We agree it's generational, or relates to eight humorless years under George W. Bush, or maybe later sites differentiate themselves from the first wave of sites by championing pretentious humorless sensationalism, not that I think Lena's writing, which she contributes to the best of the newer non-academic unconventional literary sites, is pretentious humorless sensationalism. It's certainly humorless and sensationalist but too spare and accessible to seem pretentious.

I'm not even sure what *pretentious* means these days. At one point I knew, when I was a teenager or in my twenties I may have derided semi-difficult art as *pretentious*, but now semi-difficult art helps me through the repetition of days, adds a differentiating flavor if it's humble and natural. If arrogant and ill-fitting it's terrible but if humble and natural as though rising from necessity I'm all for it. Lena's stories are humble and natural and seem to have risen out of necessity. They emerge from some unconscious region of her brain and body, her soul, her *geist*, although there's nothing Germanic about her writing other than some distant and now wholly American relation to the Brothers Grimm.

I'm not sure whose writing I like better, Feliz or Lena's, not that one needs to choose between them because they're the only non-male writers we know who drink with us sometimes. They're closer to Snare's age, and every once in a while it may be refreshing to drink with us instead of the younger guys they usually hang out with, plus they may be attracted to talking to youngish fathers who run their mouths about writing, books, kids. They've never tempted me to stray from my relatively recent marriage. I've never been tempted to stray in general but I've never been tempted to stray by them in particular. (I've never even been tempted to refer to them by their surnames.) If I were single I might consider Feliz, who's more meditative, thoughtful, touched by something good than Lena, who's on edge, teetering, distracted, disorientated, albeit without trying to *systematically disorient* her senses for the sake of what she writes. Regardless, two new non-male writer friends have joined our booth and, unlike everyone else at the table, I know that Lao and Grooms are already in the bar looking for us, ordering drinks, one of them may even be experimenting right this minute with the progressively horrific bathroom.

This is it, the moment we've all been waiting for. Lena and Feliz must know who's about to show. England sometimes texts with Lena and DMs Feliz via Twitter. Odd to text one and DM another, their preferred modes of communication. I would prefer long ruminative letters like the kind I grew up sending, especially after college, learning to write by writing long ruminative descriptive impressions directed at the recipient. Better than any MFA program would be to travel and send long ruminative descriptive handwritten impressions to friends, never thinking that the product of all that time writing would ever be seen by anyone other than the recipient, would never be posted online or collected in an anthology or retweeted or favorited or liked, no recognition or validation except at most a letter in return. The longer the letter, however, the lower the chances of receiving a similar letter in return. I never thought about that when sending long ruminative descriptive handwritten impressions to friends, never thought that friends might not have the will or capacity to reply in kind, something that often appeared in replies I received, not so much recognition or validation but *capitulation*, acknowledgement that the recipient wanted to reply with something long and ruminative and descriptive but lacked the capacity and will.

It's a matter of *will* in both senses of the word, *will* in terms of the motivating spirit that drives one to activate and accomplish something and *will* in terms of the future conjugation of the verb "to be." I love the potentiality of the word *will*, the conscious application of one's energy to change something in the future.

Lena's writing isn't all that willful in that it seems like memories of nightmares rendered in minimalist prose. I'm willful in the sense that I put myself in a position to write. That's my willful act, unlike Gibson who can't put himself in the position to write because writing requires him to control it at all times.

I exert my will to put myself in a position to relinquish control of my will. I let my will write. There's nothing subconscious about what I write, nothing dream-like, but I exert my will to relinquish control and let the necessary images and descriptive language arrive and more often than not appear on the screen or page as though channeled from some mysterious source through fingertips or pen. I exert my will to relinquish control through concentration. I concentrate in such a way that's similar to daydreaming but without letting all elements in. I exert my will to sit and concentrate in such a way that someone like Gibson might not understand since I intend to achieve relinquished control. I want to leave open a little hole in my head through which uncontrolled yet rational intelligible language can stream. Regardless, as everyone knows, writing about how one writes causes the cars on the highway to turn in on themselves at full speed and pile up in a massive clusterfuck.

I earned an unaccredited unacknowledged alternate MFA by handwriting long ruminative descriptive impressions I sent to friends. Now friends with actual official well-regarded MFAs text and DM each other, sometimes even while sitting together if the noise becomes too much, if they don't want to shout across the table, plus texts are good for snide sub-comments. Oates every once in a while whips out his phone and raises a finger in apology and says he's texting his wife when he could very well be texting Gibson about something England or Snare or I had said. He's never texted me when he's claimed to text his wife, so I believe him, although once he did text Gibson and me as Feliz was reading a long prose poem back around the time when we'd first met her. Oates sent a text that someone should pull the fire alarm. It wasn't Feliz's fault that she read last at the end of a long reading with many other readers where everyone was drinking and antsy for a change of scene. It wasn't her fault that what she'd written was made for silent solo reading, not reading aloud to restless writers not excited about hearing quiet surreal impressionistic introspective reading at that stage of the night.

Our booth at the table resembles readings at the small bar where Lao runs a little bi-monthly series. Same people, same talk, same intemperance. It's a little like church albeit in booths instead of pews. There's a convocational aspect to it, although without the reading it's really only drinking and talking. The reading is implied, at best, and tonight the reading is the celebration of Bloomsday, the arrival of Jonathan David Grooms led into the back room by a poised, triumphant Lao Guardian, delivering a familiar human in the flesh, in long white linen shirt and black shorts, black calf-high socks, and green leather sneakers unemblazoned by a recognizable brand. Here is Lao Guardian slimmer and straighter-backed than usual, strutting into the back room where we sit at one and some of another of the two Viking booths available, presenting for our pleasure the one and only Jonathan David Grooms.

XIX.

Everyone sits up and smiles and holds their glass with one hand and raises an open hand with the other, all of us other than Lena and Feliz have been waiting more than a few hours at the bar, all of us somewhat toasty including Lena and Feliz who must have been elsewhere before they arrived. Lao holds a pint of some pale golden amber beer, the hoppier the better for him, whereas Grooms has what looks like a vodka tonic or a vodka soda, or maybe a seltzer with lime. If he doesn't drink there's no way he would have agreed to meet here on a Saturday night to celebrate Bloomsday, but still once I notice that his drink might not include alcohol I become uneasy. I want him drenched, a baptism of sorts. I want us to pour beer on him after we stretch him across the heavy wooden table top of the Viking booth at which we sit. Low-level tremor has been replaced by adrenaline rush. Jonathan David Grooms's energy, mixed with Lao Guardian's energy, their combined energy raises our energy levels.

Game on, game time, show time, go time.

Up close like this in loose white linen shirt and mid-thigh black shorts, there's something about Jonathan David Grooms that suggests Euro tennis player more than writer. His limbs are long and sinewy, veins in legs clearly visible as he approaches the table, not varicosities but those of someone without much fat. His posture is so straight it suggests something wrong with his back. It wouldn't surprise me if he wears a light unobtrusive brace, like a 21st-century support corset made from breathable fabric under the flowing white-linen shirt with long sleeves rolled up almost to the elbows.

He most likely wears such a shirt because he wears a brace and a tighter shirt would reveal it. Excellent yet slightly pathological posture (Napoleonic anti-slouch?) suggests the stature of a much shorter man. With shoulders back, it's like he's preparing to trap an incoming soccer ball on his chest. His features are familiar but up close as he sits across from me at the second booth I'm surprised how delicate they are. Right from the start Lao positions Jonathan David Grooms across from me. His face is skeletal. He has a bit of stubble on the chin, a fledgling soul patch too. His thick and waxy eyebrows move as he speaks more than his mouth, and as he listens the eyebrows move too, registering the cadence and nuances of what he's heard. His once characteristic black-framed glasses are gone. He either wears contacts or had laser surgery. Grooms is smaller than I thought he would be. I'd heard he was taller but he's only about 6'1'' and slight, mostly torso, especially when seated with tanned knees beneath the table.

I have a chance to tell him about what I would have been working on if I hadn't gone out tonight to sit with friends and drink and wait for the arrival of this delicately featured, semi-skeletal man more or less my absolute contemporary, someone who's lived through the same events and evolutions I've lived through.

I say here he is, *Molly Bloom himself*, nice to meet you, yes I said yes, I said yes.

Yes I said yes *I will* yes, he says.

I say right *I will*, I love the word *will*, I love the word *will*.

I say this, realizing I'm repeating it, realizing this means I'm now officially more or less drunk, since I repeat *certain key phrases* when drunk, not the entire story or statement, just *certain key phrases*, something I rarely do when sober but if I've been drinking I tend to emphasize via repetition *certain key phrases*, in this case my love for the word *will*.

I love the word *will* I say a third time.

His large eyelids, plum-colored and wrinkled testicularly, close over his famous light green eyes and remain shut for a beat longer than a blink. He closes his eyes to protect himself from exposure to a fourth expression of my love for the word *will*, I think, but then he opens them and turns to Lao and holds up his drink and says *we have some catching up to do* and winks at me as he says it in a way that lights me up, so I raise my glass and clink it with them.

Lao drains his pint as though watering a plant. Grooms throws back his head and pours his drink into himself, most of the ice included, which he crunches as he says there's nothing like reading aloud thirty pages of stream-of-consciousness prose to parch one's throat. He says it'd taken longer than he'd thought it would and was much more difficult than he'd thought it'd be, although it was a worthwhile experience to read the final chapter so many times, not to memorize the sentences of course but to familiarize himself with their rhythms and textures.

He orders another vodka soda, specifying that he's not fussy about the brand as long as it's 80 proof. If it's crappy throw in more lime, he says, and he winks at the server, who smiles as though he said something clever.

I wonder if the server recognizes him. She knows we're all writers and Grooms may be the only writer she recognizes other than Twain, Hemingway, and Shakespeare.

I say it's incredible how few writers are recognizable as human beings, not as names but as faces, to the average person who doesn't read much. Do you think she knows who you are?

Grooms says all she needs to know is I'm house vodka diluted with plentiful lime.

Lao says what's it matter. Jon's right: celebrity is the lowest form of recognition.

Lao now calls Grooms "Jon" whereas he usually refers to him as *Grooms* or sometimes even calls him *The JDG* the way David Foster

Wallace is commonly referred to as *DFW*, adding the "the" before the initials to emphasize the literary phenomenon who by all accounts learned everything he knows from Lao back when Lao's first name was *Lou* and his surname was *Gudalian*.

He's never seemed like a Lou Gudalian, not only because he isn't Armenian. His biological father was a Scandinavian who impregnated his mother after a brief affair, so Lao looks nothing like his brothers or sisters. His nose isn't a construction of orbs but straight with a flare to the nostrils suggestive of a capacity for violence now under wraps and that really only emerges in stories about hardcore days of yore in and around rough and tumble Cleveland suburbs. He's blond unlike his siblings who are dark haired and hairier than most, whereas Lao is hairless except for thick blond hair he keeps short so his skull seems gold-plated under streetlights when I bum mentholated cigarettes from him. He smokes menthols so no one bums from him. That's how he started but now can't smoke without that cool flavor in harmonious conflict with the ember at the end. He's a blond, smooth-skinned, healthy guy who swims hundreds of laps a week, or so he claims, and also smokes these mentholated cigarettes, whose writing more often than not expresses the violence suggested in the flared nostrils. Every time he looks in the mirror he must see the violence in him, same way I see the violence in him. He remembers fights he'd been in as a kid and relives them as he brushes his teeth, and he writes to cleanse himself of those memories.

I don't often think about why he writes but he's like Snare in that he seems to write from a storehouse of anger. His mother died when he was fairly young and he was raised by an older sister and a father who resented him as much as he claimed to love him, Lao once said. The father claimed to have known about the affair with "the Nordic fucker" as the father called him. Such activities were rampant at the time. They'd read about it in Updike and wanted to live it. There was a teenage frenzy to it, Lao said his father had said. I can't remember the name of the suburb, not Shaker Heights, that was frenzied at the time, and Lao's father admitted to coming close to fathering children with other married women. For all he knew he'd fathered half the kids on the block, he'd joked, although according to Lao his mother was much more beautiful than the man who'd raised him. She was angelic and the guy who'd raised him wasn't devilish so much as a nebbish, and he became progressively nebbishy as Lao matured. There was really nothing Lao could do except change his name and fight, at first in the playground and later in gyms, flirting with boxing, training as a welterweight, but once in the ring he knew there was no way he could do it. He was eaten alive by kids who didn't know who their biological father was and didn't have the luxury of being raised by a nebbishy father and attentive siblings. There may have been a flare to his nostrils but when it came to boxing against a full-grown sixteen-year-old with arms longer than Lao's legs it was over for him. He could feel the rage he'd been throwing at the world return to him full force and felt overmatched in a way that made him want to devote himself to something else. He often jokes that he took so many blows to the head he can only manage to write weird violent prose poems with flashes of tenderness and a beating heart at all times right there up front. He can do no more than that and he aspires to no more than what he can do. But he insists he does what he can to the fullest. Also he can publish what he writes unlike everyone else other than Oates. He's at this point confident that whenever ready he'll find an independent press to publish his stuff. He is *Lao Guardian*, after all.

Independent presses are always in flux as new writers emerge and fall off and sometimes make the jump to what Lao calls a "Major," which he says with condescension, as though it's sullied by sales and marketing forces at work other than the nexus of writers who are also editors and readers, editors who are also writers and readers, readers who are also editors and writers themselves. He champions small independent releases by what he calls *minor writers*. He aspires to be a minor writer, with *minor* meaning imitation would be derided as derivative. Major writers can be imitated without fear since the writer isn't imitating a particular writer but more so working within a form with rules played by and accepted as necessary, in part to differentiate what's conventional, publishable, saleable from the unconventional, idiosyncratic, unsaleable, and unpublishable, of interest only to a smattering of sophisticates, pseudo or not, kids just out of college looking for something new and looking to join a community of sophisticates, pseudo or not, although they wouldn't express it that way. I've learned from Lao in the past few years and I think he considers me a fellow minor writer, a colleague in terms of aspiration to write something that if imitated would be considered derivative, not *original* necessarily but a set of digested impressions of the work of other writers synthesized into something *particular*.

Originality isn't the goal so much as particularity. No one's trying to do something absolutely new, that's never the intention according to Lao. I also have never been interested in trying to create something absolutely new as much as something in conversation with the work of writers I've read. That's what we, Lao and I, are most interested in, Oates too before his agent pressured him to become interested in a commercial revision of the mega-novel he's worked on for years. Oates now seems most interested in securing another publishing deal with a major New York press, whereas Lao and I, unlike Oates, Snare, and England, don't teach creative writing. I don't have a so-called terminal degree so I can't teach at the university level. Lao also doesn't teach although he'd make a fine teacher. He's taught me a good deal, has the confidence of a good teacher, of someone secure in his position in the world and sure of his opinions. He thinks he's right about everything in a way that recognizes others think they're right too, although he thinks they're wildly off-base, same as others think he's wildly off-base, so if everyone's wildly off-base why not have some confidence in the opinions that seem right to you?

Lao more than anyone recognizes that none of it matters and that it matters more than anything else. It all occupies our thoughts more than anything else in the world and we're all lucky to concern ourselves as such.

It may be the beer but I start thinking about Jonathan David Grooms not as the man sitting across from me with the delicate bone structure, expressive eyebrows, plum-colored testicular eyelids, high forehead, and a bit of an afro, but simply as *Jon*, whereas Jonathan David Grooms is the name on what he's written, the byline. The entirety of his work is *Jonathan David Grooms*, whereas the man himself is anomalous and inaccessible. Every bookstore carries several of his titles, some used bookstores seem to carry all of them in various editions, but the man himself, I have no interest in. I shouldn't have come, and then I remember I came to meet the man himself and win him over so he can help make *Throop Roebling* refer less to me than to what I write.

It's daunting to sit across from someone who has the power to flick a switch on a career. We will have an infant at home and I'll write as the kid sleeps, the wife will go back to work after a few months, I imagine she will go back to work unless Grooms shines a very bright light on my work so there's interest in the three novels and story collection I've been unable to publish since leaving New York, movie deals, several new editions, translations, odd checks appearing now and then for a couple thousand dollars, royalties for the Italian edition, Portuguese edition, Swedish and German and French editions. There's no way of knowing how it might happen, which is why I left the house tonight, to talk to Grooms, win him over, and entice him to influence the literary world on my behalf.

Grooms leans forward and directs his words into my ear so no one else can hear. Grooms says Lao has good things to say about your stuff, he's enthusiastic about it.

I can feel the warmth of his breath, can smell the vodka and lime, can smell that Grooms may have smoked some marijuana in the car when they drove from the reading to the bar. I hadn't thought he looked stoned but now that I smell it on his breath the plum shade of eyelids and expressiveness of eyebrows make me think he might in fact be stoned, just a touch, the whites of his eyes a bit bloodshot the way everyone's eyes are a bit bloodshot now.

Lao's a good man, I say.

I notice that Gibson and Oates and Lena and Feliz and England and Snare stop talking among themselves as Grooms whispers something in my ear, intended for me alone.

Grooms laughs and says indeed, indeed, indeed, absolutely right, I trust him, he says, and all are silent for a second.

Lena says hey Grooms, hey, I was just buying smokes and this old guy behind me in line said I smell a good sort of slutty, he was one of those old Italian-type guys in the neighborhood, wears a velour sweatsuit in the middle of June, and I was like god bless this neighborhood, I smell a good sort of slutty he said, so I thought I'd break that awkward silence and ask if you smell *a good sort of slutty* over where you're sitting?

Everyone titters and repeats the phrase and ascertains the degree to which it fits her. Grooms likes the phrase as much as anyone. He savors it as though he came a long way to sample exactly this variety of regional delicacy. He *is* a professional language gourmand, I suppose. He folds hands, sits straight, closes plum testicular lids over lantern-green eyes, and says the phrase several times, auditioning rhythms, each repetition emphasizing another word, a *good* sort of slutty, a good *sort* of slutty, a good sort *of* slutty, a good sort of *slutty*, he pauses to appreciate them all and asks Lena if he can name his memoir *A Good Sort of Slutty*.

I'll be forty before the end of the year, he says. It's time to publish a memoir, alas. I can't think of a better title.

Gibson says what was that, directing his question to Snare, who said something under his breath but doesn't want to repeat it and instead asks Grooms what he thinks of the city, something we're all interested in since it's a topic that comes up more than enough. The city takes some time to get to know but it's studded with gems we all now agree after years of debate.

Grooms says he knows well enough not to say what he thinks about the city because he knows his thoughts are based on false impressions. So many people talk so well about it, have so many flattering things to say about it, they defend it like a battered child, Grooms says, and also he says that he doesn't want to get into an argument with seven writers who've been drinking about the merits and drawbacks of the city they've come to love.

Grooms asks if any of us are from the city itself. Only Snare raises his hand. I say I'm from thirty miles away. Oates says he's from three thousand miles away. England says me too, the other coast. Gibson says Florida. Feliz says South Jersey. Lena says bumplefuck PA.

Grooms says he's spent enough time in enough cities to say he's truly lived in more than a dozen, all over the world, and the thing is after a time you find your spots, you find your walks, your favorite bar and restaurants and cafes and bookstores and parks, and you reduce each city from something infinite to the size of a village. If you take the streets of the city you actually live in and get rid of everything else it's the size of a village in Eastern Europe, a little Midwestern town with a flashing stoplight at the crossroads at most. We all live in small towns after a while, once we settle into a city. I mean of course that's not the definite case but it's not far off the mark. I've always loved that process of reducing the infinite to the intimate, he says.

The way he says it suggests he's said it before.

He's met more people in his life than we see in the city in a year, most likely.

He's an actor. He recites lines.

I almost start to say this outloud when Snare says how many times you say *exactly those words* to writers at bars in other cities?

I lean over the table to get a look at Snare three spots to my left. He leans over the table, pointing at Grooms, his head angled in such a way that indicates that Snare has turned the corner on the evening.

I try to cover for Snare and say I was thinking something similar, you must spend a lot of nights in situations like this, at long tables filled with writers asking questions, expecting you to say something interesting, so you must have a storehouse of statements to fall back on.

Grooms's eyes widen with bemusement and surprise, his long forehead wrinkled in a dozen fine, equal, careful furrows.

Oates says all the world's a stage, right? Almost everything I've said I said before or thought before. There's no expectation that everything must be its first and only utterance, I'm even sure I've said *first and only utterance* before.

Lao says the issue here, guys, is not whether what Jon said was *an original utterance*, the issue is that Snare is shit-housed and wants to fight our esteemed guest.

England says that sounds about right and elbows Snare who overreacts and pushes England who says you want some of this?

Gibson says *open a can of whoop ass* in the exaggerated voice of a white man.

Lena says get him England.

Feliz stares at Grooms and glitters.

Snare *glowers* in response to Grooms's presence whereas Feliz *glitters*. They do so not because Grooms is an exceptional human specimen sitting with us, sipping vodka soda with lime while wearing a loose white-linen long-sleeve shirt, they do so because he's written so many good books at this point. He isn't much older than I am, isn't much older than anyone at the table other than the two who react the most intensely, the angry young man glowering and the spacey, kind, impressionable young woman aglitter.

Oates once told me about sitting at dinner next to DeLillo, which he'll remember for the rest of his life, but sitting next to Grooms he might forget soon enough unless Snare escalates things, Feliz disrobes, Gibson forces Grooms to listen to the story of how he quit writing, unless Oates asks Grooms what he thinks about his agent demanding he rewrite his mega-novel masterpiece into a crime thriller page-turner he can't seem to write without killing the bit inside himself responsible for everything that's ever motivated him to write in the first place.

Oates whispers something in Grooms's ear and Grooms laughs and nods as Gibson pulls a quarter from behind Snare's ear as England stretches his arms up and places one arm around Lena who leans into him at first, appreciating the intimacy, until she realizes what she's doing and throws his arm off her shoulders and sits straight and says she's gonna take a big ol' sip of England's beer as tax for copping a feel.

England says for touching your shoulder you drink half my beer?

England says he just wanted everyone to feel more comfortable in the booths, thought he'd put his arms up around her and Snare on either side of him so everyone has some more room, it's all about having more room isn't it?

Lena says whatever pervert.

England looks to me, who witnessed the interaction. I say it's the most perverted thing I've seen in ages, worse than hanging brain at my bachelor party, and England chuckles and smiles at Lena who repeats several times the phrase "you were hanging brain at Throop's bachelor party?"

England hung brain at my bachelor party. A residual behavior from his time in a fraternity, some college in Maryland or Virginia. He once said he'd wanted to go to Duke, his parents were from the coastal south but he was from the Northwest and now lived in the Northeast, every once in a while scheming an escape to a southern college town where he might live in an old house with a porch on which to sip bourbon. That was the goal. He did not want to live in a submarine ten thousand leagues under the sea, in pursuit of connection with his father, or in imitation of Chester Greylag Dent, the great writer, largely because he's never heard of Chester Greylag Dent.

A porch on which to sip bourbon. He wanted to sit outside on a front porch when the weather was fine and read and sip bourbon. In this city he can sit on his stoop or his roof deck with a view of the complete city skyline, not a bad view at all, but sitting there and drinking bourbon isn't the same as sitting on a front porch, potted palms, hanging ferns, nodding good evening to families walking dogs and pushing strollers at dusk, live oaks encrusted with epiphytes abuzz with a hundred thousand contented insects.

I look over at England and say you just want a porch to sip bourbon on.

England says *that's right*, the whole reason we write, everyone here, we write with the hope of one day writing so well we're rewarded with a porch to sip bourbon on.

Grooms says but here you're drinking beer, shall we order you a bourbon and imagine a majestic antebellum front porch in South Carolina somewhere, the limbs of the surrounding gnarled oaks whispering their role in innumerable atrocities?

Lena says you're writing, not talking, you're writing, Grooms.

Grooms's forehead wrinkles in a series of fine parallel lines as his mouth contracts into a discrete circle, a pucker as innocent as an infant coaxing with cuteness its mother to give it the boob. He smiles and before he can respond England says it doesn't need to be a plantation house, I'm talking about a humble little house on a quiet street within walking distance of a downtown with a few bars and cafes and maybe an enormous bookstore, like Oxford but not in Mississippi.

Grooms says he's been to that bookstore, has read there, he loves the square and the statue of the Confederate soldier there, the one depicted at the end of *The Sound and the Fury*, when Benjy Compson screams for going the wrong way around it, Grooms says. The South has the pathos of chronic institutionalized atrocity, he says, a weight on its shoulders forever, and for a fiction writer it's a goldmine. You don't move past it, you confront it head on.

England says first we better order some bourbons.

XX.

England raises a hand like an eager student and waves it to attract the attention of our energetic server who moves faster through the crowd as every hour advances toward midnight. Not tall, she takes short choppy steps, her posture as though balancing plates on her head. She may have had a neck injury at one point. I have no memory of ever seeing her move her neck. She holds a finger up to let England know she's on the case and five minutes later I run the old rhyme through my head: beer before liquor never fear or beer before liquor never sicker? Hard stuff after soft stuff might cause problems later on. For now, immoderate ingestion of soft stuff produces bourbon we inspect like exotic toxins we clink with our neighbors. Everyone reaches to clink with Grooms and then we sip, or most of us sip, and then most of us make a face, whereas Snare and Grooms down theirs in a gulp, almost like a duel, neither wanting to blink.

Grooms says I rarely drink brown alcohol and do not linger when I do.

Snare says *whew* and wipes his mouth with his sleeve, a happy go-lucky cowboy after a long hot day rustling steer. I can't imagine Snare rustling steer, and I also don't like seeing more flammable material poured on the fire burning in him now. At best, he'll wake tomorrow on England's couch after vomiting in England's toilet, head shattered, mouth feeling like a mouse died in there, stomach heaving, doing everything he can to drag his ass to his car and make it home without incident. At worst, homicide and/or suicide are now in play. Yes, at this relatively early point in the evening, if he keeps drinking like this, he might kill someone or kill himself or simply choke on his vomit.

Give me your keys, I say. I think it's time for you to give me your keys.

Snare says why you?

I say because you'll stay with John tonight and I'll have your keys tomorrow nearby when you want to head home.

Snare says I'm not giving you my keys.

He holds them close to his face, one hand over an eye to better focus as he bats at them with the backs of his fingers, like these keys are the prettiest keys in the land as far as Snare is concerned, pretty pretty pretty keys, lovely keys to the kingdom of Snare. One starts his car, one opens his front door, another opens his back door, one for his office door at the university, one for his childhood home he keeps for good luck. The way he bats them around in front of his face makes me think of a loaded gun. Of all the pieces of metal in the room, of all the concealed weaponry (and there could be a good deal of it since the bar's filling up and it's Saturday night so the crowd doesn't consist of innocuous regulars) the key Snare holds is the trickiest. No one seems to hear us, everyone talks above and around us, as I intervene to defuse the situation.

I say *dude*, thinking that will convince him. *Dude* will do it, *dude* will let him know I mean business. I say give me the car key, you can keep the other keys, I don't care about your office key, house keys, whatever, just give me the car key.

Snare tries to engage Gibson in some talk across the table, all while dangling his keys in front of his face, like he's trying to tantalize Gibson into pouncing on them. Gibson follows each sip of bourbon with a swig of beer. Snare calls him *dude*, mocking me, his inflection intended to attract attention more than threaten coercion.

But Gibson chats with Oates and Grooms. Gibson leans across Oates who leans back as Grooms leans over the table to better hear

Gibson say something about Dublin that animates Grooms in response.

I tap England on the shoulder, reaching behind Lena and Feliz, who talk about how the last time they drank bourbon Lena got all shit-housed whereas Feliz considers it an old man's drink, the sort of thing old white male alcoholics like England drink.

England protests, says he's only a few years older than her.

Feliz says it depends how you define a few.

I tap England on his rounded right shoulder again, this time with knuckles instead of fingertips, and he leans back and we try to talk behind Lena and Feliz about Snare but then they lean back and so I lean forward but England doesn't also lean forward so I lean back again and when I do it turns out he's leaned forward, so I lean forward right as he leans back and then I lean back and reach behind Lena and Feliz and lean them forward for a second, saying excuse me.

England says that makes it easy, just push 'em out of the way.

Lena says you guys better not be talking about me behind my back.

Feliz says something similar.

I say it's not always about you, and to England I say get his keys, his car key at least.

England says why?

I say *seriously*?

England says is he any more wrecked than usual?

I say just get it, I have a bad feeling this time.

England says you're a control freak.

I say friends don't let friends kill themselves and others in cars.

England says we let each other kill ourselves and others every day of our lives.

I say what's that supposed to mean?

Lena says *hey guys* who you talking about killing back there?

Feliz says *yeah* sounds like you're planning a murder, and she says it loud enough that Oates and Grooms and Gibson and Lao stop talking about the Bloomsday celebration in Dublin and look across the way.

Lao leans across the table toward me and directs his speech at everyone for full effect. He says look guys I'm not bringing writers from out of town to hang out with you if the first thing you do after we order a round of bourbon is conspire to take them out.

Grooms says wouldn't be the first time.

Snare says who you think you are, Rushdie?

Everyone laughs, most likely just to laugh, and then Grooms says no seriously I was threatened in Italy not because I had insulted Catholicism or their beloved practice of living at home with their mothers well into their thirties. I was threatened by a young Italian journalist who didn't believe that writers should be honored and interviewed. He believed writers, especially well-known writers, should in fact be abused. In very good English, in a very sexy Italian accent, he said when writers write good books they should receive thirty blows to the back with a whip, they should be *systematically punished* for every critical success, and instead of winning awards for their work, they should be *systematically punished* for every success, *systematically punished* for every glowing review, the bigger the success the bigger the punishment. So I said I suppose I should take that knife in your hand as a compliment, Grooms says. Of course there were a lot of people around so I wasn't too worried but then the enraged Italian journalist said something about how I had to pay for my bestsellers and award-winners. He said something about how he was only doing what's right and then he rushed me with his knife. I had never been threatened like this of course, never mugged, never even in fights as a child, but now I was being assaulted with a deadly weapon, instead of being interviewed I was being assaulted. Sure, sure, interviews sometimes feel *assaultive* but nothing like this was expected in an elegant hotel in Milan, a small ballroom, empty except for a few dozen Italian literary types, cameramen for television, and right in front of everyone this guy rushes me with knife held high to stab me in the skull or bring it down with maximum force into my heart, Grooms says. No one moved, like maybe they were all in on it or maybe everyone was as shocked as I was. It was truly one of those moments that slowed down as he seemed to rush me through a pool of gelatin. He seemed to run through an expanse between us of invisible mud. All I had was my drink, a flute of champagne, and as he approached my instinct took over and sent the champagne at him and struck him in the face, right in the eyes, and he stopped in his tracks as though it woke him from a nightmare. He gasped as though surfacing from a long dive underwater, and then everyone mobbed him and handed me the knife the crazy young journalist had meant to plunge into my chest. It was the strangest thing to confront that level of threat in person. I say *strange* because ever since I've wanted something like it to happen again, at every reading when it's time for Q&A or when I'm signing books I'm disappointed no one tries to drive a hunting knife into my heart. I tell this story, and, no, this isn't the first or second or even *thirtieth* time I've told this story, Grooms says, directing his words at Snare, I tell this story because I know how much anger is out there. It's one of the comparatively minor burdens of having some success. Much of the anger seems directed at people like me, if not me specifically. There's more than enough appreciation and even adoration but I know that more than a few obscure corners of the world abhor me, and I welcome it to an extent. I don't have a death wish but I understand the impulse to want to take me out. If I weren't in my position at this point in my life I would not have been as gentlemanly as most of you have been tonight, most of you other than that one, Grooms says, nodding toward Snare and giving him a wink, which wins Snare over same as it seems to win everyone over, but also now all of you are well aware that if threatened and subsequently rushed tonight I intend to neutralize my assailant with a quick flip of the wrist and a proper dousing with whatever drink is close at hand.

Grooms mimes tossing his drink at us, one and all, and it seems less like self-defense than anointment, like he's baptizing with hypothetical booze, neutralizing player-hate.

Everywhere he goes he must be assaulted by writers and readers who know who he is, who have read everything he's written, who have seen him speak, who have spent time talking and thinking about him and yet he has no idea who these people are and what they might want. Some might harbor resentment as a result. They know so much about him and think so much about him and he acts as though they don't even exist! Some unbalanced types might seek a balancing of the scales, they might want more from Grooms than he can provide a single reader of his work, particularly another writer.

Snare seems neutralized for now if not more sober. He raises his glass in a toast to "assaulting famous writers" and everyone laughs and says *hear hear.*

I say just so you know there's no conspiracy, I'm just worried about a certain someone driving home tonight and I want to get his keys.

Everyone looks over at Snare since he's the only one of us who doesn't live within walking or biking distance.

Snare says *fuck that* with emphasis sufficient to drain the cheer of the toast.

I say you should not be driving tonight, right?

Snare says you should not be driving tonight.

I explain to Grooms that I live around the corner and haven't driven in weeks.

To Snare I say either quit drinking now and not leave for hours or continue to drink but relinquish your keys to me or Lao. That's the situation. Deal?

Snare says no deal.

Gibson says seems fair, you can pick from a bunch of places to stay.

Oates says it's a no-brainer, hand over your keys and text your wife you'll be home in the morning.

Snare says she didn't want him coming home wrecked after sleeping on England's kitchen floor.

England says we'll inflate the airbed and pull it out on the back deck so you can sleep under whatever stars make it through the light pollution.

Snare says enough, enough, out of the question.

Lao says if you give me the keys you can come over tomorrow morning and meet my son and if the timing's right have breakfast with Grooms and me and Linda too. She makes a mean breakfast taco.

Snare says I like a mean breakfast taco.

Lao says *the meanest*, with spicy sausage, fluffy eggs, and home-made pico de gallo.

Snare says sounds fancy.

Grooms says give me your keys and I will personally deliver them to you in the morning if you miss breakfast. I will hunt you down wherever you lie asleep, covered in vomit or not, and I will return the loaded weapon in your hands. Yes, it is a loaded weapon right now. Those keys are dangerous and they're best in someone else's pockets. Let's put them in my pocket, a fine temporary home for your precious keys.

Snare dangles them in front of himself and flips them up and lets them fall into his palm, where they sprawl like an electric spider suddenly unplugged.

Snare says on one condition.

Grooms says within reason.

Snare says I'll hand over my keys if you look at my book.

Grooms says published or manuscript?

Snare says a manuscript I've been working on for a long time and can't find agents for.

Grooms says I can't say I'll offer salvation by way of a good word or two of advice, I've never been able to do that before, but I'll look it over. I can't say I'll read every word but if it seems promising I'll pass it on to someone who might be willing to work with you. Forward it to me at groomsburger at yahoo dot co dot UK.

Snare says like cheeseburger?

Grooms nods with an air of exaggerated dignity and gravity and nobility. *Groomsburger* it is and has always been, he says. I have others but that is the one I use.

Snare says groomsburger it is. He squints at his phone, thumbs something into it, and then says you should have it now, means a lot, good looking out.

Grooms says you're forgetting one thing.

Snare says right.

He drops the keys. England slides them across the table to Grooms who catches them as they fall into the gap between the two tables.

Lena says so how drunk do I have to get before I can send you my manuscript?

Lao, attentive handler that he is, says I didn't bring him here so he can leave with a half-dozen novel manuscripts.

Grooms says it's no inconvenience at all since I'm under no obligation to respond but if I detect some promise I can do the right thing and try to help and limit some of the anger out there among writers having trouble seeing their writing take the next step. I can't write their stuff for them but I can forward it to the proper authorities if it seems like their troubles have been unjust. Please realize however that for the most part the trouble they're having is not so much with entities in publishing, a varied lot with heroes and villains like any occupation. The trouble younger angrier writers are having so often is with themselves. They're angry not at the publishing industry but at themselves. The young Italian intent on stabbing me could have killed himself but instead took his trouble out on me. Instead of working through his trouble, instead of seeing it as an obstacle he had to overcome with ingenuity and persistent effort, he took the easy way out, that is he tried to take *me* out, that's why I'm more than happy to use whatever authority's been vested in me by the gods responsible for literary production to relieve our friend here of the keys to his car, that seems like something I can do to save him, although with his own work there's little I can do if he hasn't already saved himself in a sense. No one can save anyone else when it comes to the work we do. If something is published and promoted that's undeserving, it's a curse worse than eternal decline. Undeserving acceptance destroys hope, and hope is the one thing unpublished writers have to live for. It's much simpler and better to hope for that initial publication than trying to write and publish after that initial publication. My case of course has been a lucky one, but even then I have to contend with responses in the press, I have to spar with interviewers, I sometimes hear what people say and it affects the next day's work, whereas if you work in critical silence you can focus on what you write, and that seems like a blessing, yet it seems like a blessing every last one of you would relinquish as soon as possible.

Oates explains his situation with his agent, how he's whittling his unacknowledged mega-novel masterpiece down to a crime novel thanks to what amounts to a threat from his agent to drop him if he insists she go out with *Death by Jacaranda*.

Oates's face has some of the satanic innocence of a possessed doll once he gets going but he doesn't get angry the way Snare does. The possessed doll aspects conceal no meat cleaver. He's never passive aggressive or even simply *aggressive* aggressive, and he never raises his voice. Instead he speaks circles around an irritant like a boa constrictor of language, and then he squeezes, repeating and refining conclusions until he's reduced the irritant's bones to consumable mush.

Oates says when he submitted *Death by Jacaranda* to his agent after working on it daily for hours for years, the agent took several months before she responded that the novel came off as a slur to her. Oates says his agent said she considered his manuscript *a slur*, this novel he'd worked on and put everything he'd had into it about his teen years in Whittier, a suburban Los Angeles County town out east where the streets are lined with jacaranda trees. He put everything he had into it, every sentence written in blood, he says. Oates says he wanted to apply the aesthetic and psychic charge *2666* gave him to memories of growing up in Nixon's hometown, the whole nascent skater thing, like *Lord of the Flies* but with multiple perspectives, a polyphonic sequence of thematically intertwined novellas. He thought he'd written a good and important book, Oates says, at this point mostly speaking to Grooms and me and Lao, our side of the table. Everyone else has heard the story before and rides a wave of bourbon and beer away from what Oates says about the good and important book he's written.

He quotes Flaubert about how we read books not for instruction or entertainment but to live. Oates says he wrote a book he wanted readers *to live*, he wrote into existence a place where readers could live their lives, an adventure novel and a novel that confronts the abyss, like what Bolaño said, Oates says, about how there are two varieties of American novel, the adventure novel like *Huck Finn* and the abyss novel like *Moby-Dick*, so Oates set out to breed adventure and abyss. Instead of "oases of terror in a desert of boredom," instead of the three-hundred pages of murdered women in northern Mexico, instead of the obsessive hunt for the white whale in Melville, his abyss involved fault lines, shifting plates, the colossal scale of continental drift threatening to show how fragile lives are, especially since the novel focuses on teenagers, skaters, punkers, rockers, some less mainstream than others, all straddling fault lines in lives they barely understand, Oates says. They barely understand these fault lines and barely understanding drives their adventures yet all the while the abyss is right there, ocean, desert, mountains, cruelties of youth, the essential sadism of teenage boys, it's all in there and I wrote my ass off, Oates says. *I wrote my ass off* but my agent treated the whole thing like a slur, like I'd insulted her. She found thirty pages in the nine-hundred page manuscript that might be developed into something she could sell, a crime thriller. I offered the title *California Über Alles* and she jumped at it and said that's the sort of thing she's thinking, like James Ellroy without short choppy sentences. So that's what I'm working on now, a crime novel like James Ellroy without short choppy sentences. But I have no interest in the genre. It's impossible not to parody it at every turn, impossible not to write a *comedic* crime novel. It's challenging work in a way that feels more like a job than an art. Like you said it's better to have that hope, to write without critical responses, *till human voices wake us and we drown*, said Eliot, something like that. *I hear the mermaids singing each to each, I do not think they'll sing to me*, that shit is so sad, Oates says. Exclusion from the miraculous, that's exactly it. Fear I'll spend the rest of my writing life on the beach with trousers rolled up thinking I'm no Prince Hamlet. It's been great to hear the mermaids singing, a miraculous phenomenon I'm lucky to have experienced. But that's it. That's as far as it goes.

The whole time Oates talks Grooms looks into his drink, shakes his head in recognition, nods, grimaces, smiles, eyebrows and forehead registering and most likely storing the details of the story.

Grooms says do you have the original manuscript you sent to your agent? I'd like to look at it. I could pass it on to my agent if you'd like, that is, if I disagree with your agent.

Oates says of course of course that would be fantastic, I have it somewhere in my email, and he starts thumbing his phone and says you still with the Jackal?

Grooms says I've made the jump from the Jackal to the Devil himself. I'm now represented by Beelzebub, Lord of Darkness. It says exactly that on his card, red satin emblazoned with pitchforks and harmless little flames that lick off its edges. Pretty cool really. I made the jump a few years ago, Grooms says and then takes a swig of beer. He doesn't even take fifteen percent, Grooms says, you just open a vein and sign in blood on the dotted line of this enormous sheaf of parchment streaked with ancient calligraphy in miniscule illegible script and then you sign beneath all these names you recognize. It's the highest literary honor to sign this document, better than the Nobel. Philip Roth's name was right above mine. How else do you think he got his last few novels published? He had a good agent, a great agent, the best possible agent. He also made the jump to our agent toward the end. He doesn't take on many clients since he represents into perpetuity. Shakespeare, Milton, Blake, all the old Romantic poets, Austen, the Brontës, and George Eliot, Dickens, Tolstoy, Dostoevsky, Chekhov, Gogol, Mann, Musil, Joyce of course, Faulkner, Fitzgerald, Gaddis, Cheever, Bernhard, Pynchon, DeLillo, Wallace, all men since the 20th Century. He just stopped representing women at one point. No Virginia Woolf, no Iris Murdoch, no Susan Sontag, no Toni Morrison. I asked him about it and he said he only represented dead white men from this point forward, regretted signing the Brontës and George Eliot he'd said, and when I asked about me and Pynchon, DeLillo, and Roth he said he took a long view of things. We were alive now but in the grand scheme of things we'd spend much more time dead and of course I couldn't disagree with him, Grooms says, deadpan.

Oates says so you'd send *Death by Jacaranda* to Satan himself to see if he wants to represent it? Oates takes a big swig of beer and says so what happens if he wants to take it on?

Grooms says you know the old saying *damned if you do, damned if you don't,* I'm sure it was coined by a writer who he turned down, or a writer who turned him down. It doesn't matter much one way or the other. If you want to work with him, if you're willing to work with him, you're damned, I'm damned, Lao's totally damned, the angry young man over there is damned, this observant Throop fellow here is damned. We'd all sell our souls in a second if we could sign a document in ancient illegible calligraphy that ensured inclusion in the high-lit canon. We'd sign it even if it meant eternal damnation. We'd hesitate, sure, but in the end we'd see the names on the scroll—Flaubert, Stendhal, Balzac, Perec—we'd see the names and whatever compelled us to write in the first place would sign after we dipped the quill, the same one used by Shakespeare and Cervantes, into our arms for sufficient ink.

Oates says I sent you the manuscript. Didn't know you were making a point about ambition. Goes to show that even as you were saying what you were saying I was excited to get my manuscript to you, hoping for a break to keep me from having to write this non-satirical crime thriller about skater kids in the Reagan years.

Grooms says you can always write both? I'll see what I can do with the mega-novel. I mean do you have any idea how much cash the *Fifty Shades* series brings in for publishers, *Twilight*, *Harry Potter*, every once in a while they hit on these blockbusters that to my mind make it so they have a moral obligation to publish novels that might not be saleable but the sort that's written for a reason and needs its chance to meet as many readers as possible.

I say like pharmaceutical companies that develop treatments for rare diseases. *Orphan drugs* they're called because there's not much of a market for them and they cost as much to produce as drugs for diabetes and cardiovascular disease. So you're saying publishing companies have a moral obligation to commit a percentage of their blockbuster profit to the publication of orphan novels, books without an obvious shot at making much money but are rare in a way.

Grooms says publishing companies would argue that ninety percent of what they publish, especially literary titles, are expected to lose money, but the thing is, these books are expected to lose money not because they're weird or idiosyncratic or offbeat or peculiar or sublime failures. They're for the most part conventional fiction expected to lose money because such books have always lost money. Every once in a while one does well and is picked up by a major book club or spreads by word of mouth but generally they have no shot of becoming a phenomenon because there's nothing original about them. That's why my contracts now state that my publisher must take six titles I recommend for every book I publish. It's like my own little book club except I take hundreds of thousands of dollars less than I could and make sure the money goes to the publication of these titles, and not just to advances but to promotion too.

Lao says ever think of starting your own press?

Grooms says the second I start thinking about starting my own press, even funding my own press, I begin to worry about finances and whether someone I trust is embezzling or slacking or misrepresenting everything I thought we stood for, so with this arrangement I pay for the advances and marketing out of my own advance and marketing and otherwise have no connection with the books they publish with that money except that I can recommend manuscripts and writers and in general they keep me apprised and seem to appreciate it whenever I forward something to them, whenever I drop by to chat about authors they might want to consider, for example our friend Lao here. I'm actively petitioning on his behalf.

Lao directs his thumbs at his chest and says he's *actively petitioning* on this guy's behalf, and Grooms says of course I'm *actively peti-*

tioning on Lao's behalf. He's the sort of writer who requires *active advocacy*. Agents and editors take one distracted look at his stuff and move on. They see concentration on language, prose poem fiction, juxtaposition of the sacred and the profane, and their default reaction is *I don't know how to sell this*, as though it's something without precedent upon the earth. The current model and approach doesn't satisfy readers since it fills bookstores with identical tones in books with identical covers of naked female necks, of bare backs, of bare legs, of identical script intertwined with flowers or some other decorative aspect vaguely relevant to the title. Agents know how to sell the current approach to editors whose sales colleagues know how to put on the shelves of bookstores that then have no chance of interesting half the world's population, that is, men who read but are so rarely presented with anything they might want to read. I don't mean *Fight Club* or gratuitously violent stuff. I mean writing that might appeal to men, that's masculine in its sensibility. European editors still publish this sort of thing. Novels about young men in cities figuring their way out, autobiographical coming-of-age stories that seem to have no plot other than the undulating and circuitous yet rising development of the narrator, but I've said too much, I don't want to start railing about the difference between European and American publishing. The difficulty now is that never in the history of humanity have so many people considered themselves writers, never have so many people been certified fiction writers, never have so many people spent so much time typing in Microsoft Word and sending what they write to a hundred thousand online and offline publications, everyone addicted to the instant gratification of posting their writing on these sites or on their own blogs and then updating their social media profiles with a link to it and then watching the update accrue likes, every hour another few likes until there are dozens of likes and they feel good about what they wrote, although most people who liked the update with the link to the story didn't read the story, just liked that the writer had posted a link to something they'd written, and then the writer with all this positive reinforcement thinks they're on par with writers who've dedicated their lives to writing, who would have done it without the technology that made it all so easy. That's the point, really, it's all so easy now, there aren't enough obstacles, and so it seems like for what would've been every story out there decades ago now there are a hundred stories, and everyone who then doesn't make it from that first rung of validation to the next rung and the one after that and the one after that becomes embittered, their enthusiasm comes up against the wall of the reality that their work is adequate at best, undernourished at worst, and here hundreds of writers give up and the few who go on have a chance, but only a chance. There's no predictor for success other than endurance, perseverance, or put another way, quitters never win, but I'm talking too much, it's been a while since I've had anything to drink, and tonight I've had wine, vodka, bourbon, and beer.

Lao says we've only just begun, and then he says that what Grooms said sounds absolutely right, so many writers seem to spend the majority of their time praising other writers, hoping to receive praise when it comes time for the writers they praised to praise them, they expect their praise for others will return to them, they live by the Golden Rule, do unto others et cetera, and so what you get is a praise-a-thon, everyone praising everyone and where does that get anyone? It's not entirely true that absolutely everyone's praising everyone but that's the perception, everyone praising everyone, everyone drumming up support for themselves by drumming up support for others. It's maddening for those who don't recognize it for what it is because it seems like everyone's lost their minds, everyone is calling everyone a genius, a great writer, an excellent writer, the best writer, all these superlatives tossed around like it's sports commentary, everyone's a great experimentalist, the best around, the best unknown writer working today under the cloak of darkness and shadows and writing under a rock, the best young writer writing to-day even if the young writer is forty-five and has kids in their teens. The thing that gets lost in all this and that might be of some impor-tance to writers is *truth*, the whiff of truth, the scent of truth. I've al-ways said that if I can't trust how a writer talks about books and other writers then I can't trust what they write since it goes to show they have a faulty bullshit detector, as Hemingway said. You've got to have *a fail-safe bullshit detector*, a fail-safe bullshit detector you can't turn off for a time while you compose blurbs about other writers, when you write status updates about other writers that are so fawning that even the faultiest bullshit detectors out there go off. Some writers put word out into the world about how much they love a writer and all the bullshit detectors go off at once but no one calls anyone on their bullshit. That's the thing: you want someone to police every-thing and say no, sorry, what you wrote is total bullshit, the enemy of the truth, but there's no one willing to take on that work. Some-times someone tries to write a rough review of someone's work, but no one polices positive blurbs and updates and calls people out as untrustable.

Grooms says is that a word?

I say yeah it is if Lao says it, even if it's not a word it's a word, and then I shut up as Grooms goes to the bathroom and Lena takes his seat after Feliz goes to the bathroom and England slides over and suggests a smoke and Lao stands to join us as Snare curls into himself drunk texting or drunk tweeting who knows what.

XXI.

It's not my responsibility, I say to England, making our way through the barroom, it's not my duty to police what Snare transmits tonight.

England says of course it is, you got him this drunk, riling him up and taking his keys. He lives out on the Main Line, England says, you know what that means to take away the car keys of someone who lives out there, plus now you've forced him to stay with me.

I say there goes your plans for a three-way with Feliz and Lena.

He laughs and gives me a long white cigarette I try to light but immediately smell burning cardboard and see a small fire inches from my face. The filter's as white as the rest of it and if I light it without proper attention there's a fifty-fifty chance of lighting the filter instead of the correct end. I throw it to the curb where it smolders and ask for another. England finds it funny, like I'm a child unable to properly light my cigarette, like this act of generously handing down another cigarette gives him the upper hand. I owe him now, I think he thinks.

England says you only do that when you're about done.

I say I've only just begun.

England says uh oh, and I improvise a gesture suggesting we're about to enter Bloomsday hyperspace, a swooshing forward propulsion with torso and arms directed at the skyscrapers to the northwest in the distance. Now the anchors are lifted, now we're airborne.

England asks what I think of Grooms.

Fuck that guy, I say.

England says huh?

Kidding, I say. It's weird when you meet these famous writer types, I always feel like they feel pressure to perpetuate their identity as famous writers, to drop knowledge, wisdom, that sort of thing. Grooms seems comfortable for the most part but I'm not sure how well he'll handle his drink.

England says I noticed that too, he's not quite built for more than three.

Lao pops out and lights a long menthol, which I prefer at this point to England's Parliaments. Lao says *hey guys how ya been*, a phrase I expect from him and he expects us to expect him to say, I think, since he always says it and I always raise my arms a little to acknowledge the ritual of another cigarette outside a bar with Lao, who nods a lot and pulls on his shirt like it's hot when it's so perfect it's like the weather doesn't exist, the ideal atmosphere.

Lao says I'm not sure if I should get him out of here or let him do what he wants even if he'll blame me tomorrow.

England says he's a grown man.

I say we waited for him longer than he's been here, I'd feel cheated if he left soon.

Lao says boo hoo.

I say run him out there a little longer, plus I think he's got something going with Feliz.

Lao says *right*, you caught that too.

England says I didn't see anything of the sort.

I realize then that England may have feelings for Feliz. It seems like England too is surprised by his tone of voice and tries to cover it up.

England says I never thought she'd be the star-struck type.

Both Lao and I say *Feliz?*

Lao says I'd expect she'd be more star struck than anyone.

England says *I don't know*, I think she's better than that.

I say if you were a young lady wouldn't you be interested in Grooms?

England says who says I'm not?

Lao says you're neither a lady nor all that young, son.

England says suck it.

I say so Grooms, huh? A second ago you seemed into Feliz.

England says *whatever it takes*.

Lao says I never knew.

Wait a second, I say, you'd cuddle up with Grooms?

England says *I don't know*, and he says it in his characteristic sing song, the phrase more benefit of the doubt than anything Socratic, the last vowel rounded and sustained, a pleasant reverberation issuing from a round head. I picture a Venn diagram with one circle representing England and another circle representing Grooms overlapping to create a shaded area representing their intermingling parts.

England says I don't know, desperate times call for desperate measures, and not every day do you get the chance to do someone of his stature, even if he's a dude, a bit of a drawback, albeit outweighed by a lifetime of potential benefit. What do I have to lose at this point?

The virginity of your most odiferous orifice, Lao says.

England says wow.

I say weren't you in a frat? Was there a lot of that there?

England says our slogan was beer, bitches, and bros.

Lao says watch football, chug Old Swill, circle-jerk the bros, drunk enough to write it off.

England says enjoy your fantasies about frats but the *bitches* element was pretty big.

Lao says strike out at the kegger, blow your roommates.

England says not like there's anything wrong with that, and we all laugh, and England says but no really it wasn't anything like that. I'm not saying I've done anything like that in the past just that tonight if it comes down to it, I don't know, you never know. England trails off and exhales smoke toward the skyscrapers.

I say two roads diverge on a Bloomsday night and the rest depends on whether you seduce Grooms and win him over to support your writing. If you win him over you gain all sorts of recognition you'll always wonder if it wasn't wholly deserved, wasn't in part based on whatever went on in some hotel room one early summer night, but if you don't do anything you'll always wonder what might have happened if you managed to do him.

Lao says yes there are two paths you can go by, one leads to fortune and fame and the other to obscurity, bitterness, frustration, sorrow, and an early death, either self-inflicted or brought about by booze and pills.

England says there are two types of people in this world, those who believe in idiotic reductive dualities and those who don't.

I laugh and say like yin and yang sharing the same circle, night and day sharing the same sky, body and soul in the same person.

Lao says are you going to say it? Are you going to say your favorite Milton line now?

I say if you insist: *light and darkness in perpetual round.* (It's something I remember from *Paradise Lost*, a perfectly weighted phrase.)

Lao whoops and with his cigarette draws in the air a circle with a winding slash through it and with his free hand he punches two holes in what he's drawn.

England says that's all well and good but I have to care for Snare tonight since Grooms has his keys, unless we all go back to my place and Grooms and I cuddle as Snare passes out in the bathroom.

I say care for Snare.

Lao says a Snare scare.

England says anyone checked what he's been posting?

Lao says my phone don't do that.

England thumbs his phone a few times, says oh man.

I say what?

England says we've got to get that phone from him, he's committing digital hari kari.

I don't feel like accessing Snare's profiles so I rely on England to relay the worst but England won't say what Snare's been posting, just keeps scrolling and hooting and grimacing, saying no he didn't, no he didn't.

I say let's have some examples.

England says trust me it's better if I keep this to myself, don't look at your phone, let's just go get his phone from him.

I say what's Snare saying that's so bad?

Lao says he talking shit about Grooms?

Lao seems at times electrocuted, like his internal wiring shocks his system and causes twitchy shivers. Whatever causes this current, it goes through Lao as though we aren't enjoying a perfect mid-June evening but a torrential sleet storm in January.

Snare might be sending me up too, lampooning me, criticizing my steadiness despite consumption of umpteenth beers, accusing me of superficial magnanimity founded on easy worthless silence, or maybe Snare limits his outbursts to anti-Groomsian commentary, maybe Snare's most comprehensive and representative self-expression requires him to unleash upon the online netherworld bursts of caustic, misspelled, character-restricted updates and tweets?

Lao will find hate speech directed at his old friend and guest of honor more hateful than if Snare lambasted Lao himself, and the promulgation of hatefulness could become combustible. Something about Lao that I find surprising are his claims of a violent past. We've all lived for much longer than we've known each other. None of us knew each other when we were younger, in our late teens or early twenties. Stories Lao tells of days of youthful yore involve hardcore rock, freestyle rap battling, brawling, anger expressed through aggressive music, aggressive behavior, although I don't see how aggression still occupies his body. He seems free of aggression, a father, a hard-working ad man employed by a local university. He says his ads run on the sides of buses, on billboards, online. He's occupied by son and family life now, possessed by it. No one offers a better impression of family life than Father Guardian, no one's a better cheerleader for family life than Papa Lao. Whenever we talk about fatherhood I become possessed with it too, apprehensions exit, replaced by excitement, the opposite of anticipatory anxiety, impending good news, like the summer that stretches ahead now that it's June 16 and the weather has settled and the temperature won't drop under forty again until October. The summer ahead is more than a season, it's wide-open vernal expansiveness you don't think will ever shut down, the spring and summer eternal.

There was good old-fashioned apprehension and anxiety in the fall and winter. Our identities were shifting so quickly. I was a single man alone and then a married man and now an expectant father. The sleek single woman I'd fallen for is now a married expectant mother, her most recent weeks concerned with making sure the baby's head points downward in proper birthing position. It had been breech last time they looked, she's been doing exercises to shift her hips above her heart, arranging pillows and balancing on them in ways that seems dangerous for the kid if she rolls off pillows and weight comes down on belly when she falls off couch or bed. I don't see how she keeps herself from taking our largest sharpest kitchen knife and performing an elective improvised Cesarean operation on herself when sleep-deprived in the kitchen, middle of the night, craving fats in the latter stages of fetal development, real bacon, not turkey bacon. She forced me to buy *real bacon* last weekend and it was ridiculously crispy and set off the smoke alarms but was worth the grease in the pan she insisted I save for later use in an old jelly jar.

I had claimed that in the last month of her pregnancy I wouldn't have more than two drinks per session but here I am after way more than three with wife more than eight months pregnant. She expresses it in weeks that never mean much to me, thirty-three weeks, thirty-four weeks, thirty-five weeks, she says. Months are stages of the moon. Nine months means full moon. I'm not sure how many weeks a normal term lasts, thirty-six weeks equals nine months times four weeks but that can't be correct, my math skills are weak, but she's far along and ready to roll at any time. Bloomsday won't be the day, plus it's approaching midnight so Bloomsday definitely won't be the day, and even if it happens tomorrow morning hugely hungover I'll take five ibuprofens and guide her to a cab we'll take ten blocks north to the hospital, we can even walk it if we want to, if she can.

Father Guardian always says the baby will come when the baby wants to come and then it will sleep sixteen hours a day for a year. We'd have time to read and watch movies, do whatever we want to do, except there'll be a bundle of swaddled joy in the bassinet. It's not so hard, Father Guardian always says, because it's what you want to do, you do it on instinct, you do it because it must be done, you do it because the baby is crying and you'll do anything to comfort him, a boy in Father Guardian's case, the only one among us with a son.

We've envisioned our seven-year-old boy playing with a nine-year-old Guardian boy, tossing a ball in the park as we stand on the sidelines and talk about writing, shooting hoops as we lean on tall chain-link fences around the courts and talk about books, the boys kicking a soccer ball as we sit in the first-base side dugout of the softball field as it drizzles and the boys practice slide tackling in the slick grass of the outfield, always ready for a kid to open a vein as he slides through broken glass. I shouldn't be thinking so far ahead, worrying about the boy tearing open his leg while sliding in the slick grass of the softball-field outfield. I always tell the wife not to worry about the future so much, not to worry about what the school system will be like when the kid is old enough for high school, not to worry what the neighborhood will be like in fifteen years. We have no idea what it will be like, what the city will be like, what the kid will be like, what we'll be like, what our lives will be like. We might have to move for work to support ourselves and the kid, there might not be jobs for us in the city, we might want to move to a town with trees and grass and paths through woods, we might want to live in wilderness cut off from humanity, on a desert island in the middle of the woods, we might be in a position to work from home full-time from anywhere. I can't even see a few weeks ahead to the due date, more or less the Fourth of July.

Whenever asked about the due date I say it's the Fourth of July although it's actually the seventh. I heard seventh and assumed they said fourth, the seventh of July would work too, a pair of sevens, an extra hot day I hope, the sort on which sunshine comes down in sheets and you stick to the shadows when you walk around the city, the bright sides of the streets abandoned. I hope it's a blindingly bright hot day when we make it to the hospital, the sun at full force.

Welcome to the world, my dear. So much light upon our golden child.

There's a feeling of fulfillment even if the baby hasn't yet come, the walking and reading and writing work a luxury, something I hope to continue, my secret source of strength, faith, spiritual sustenance, something like that, something neither nonexistent nor unprotected.

England with his unprotected aspiration, wearing his writerly self on his sleeve. I don't want to see him so desperate he'll seduce Jonathan David Grooms. Gibson claiming he's done, his writing spirit extinguished. Oates writing commercial fiction instead of what he needs to write. Snare consumed by a fury he stokes in his belly, like stroking a rabid cat. Even Lena and Feliz seem to have emerged from the winter and spring transformed, or maybe I know them better now than I did last fall. I'd heard how Feliz had been raised by young urban hippie punks, without the privileges a lot of us take for granted. Lena too hadn't been raised by mild-mannered suburbanites, more like country folk who'd migrated from the city a generation or two ago, country folk with vestiges of city life still in them. I wasn't sure what to call it but warded it off when I saw it. I couldn't help it, a timbre in the voice, a flattening of vowels, an intensity of attack always at somewhat elevated volume that made me miserable. I'm overly sensitive to sound and light, not pathologically hypersensitive, sensitive to it maybe more than most people, or maybe everyone is as sensitive as I am to sound and light but everyone's more able to overcome sensitivities or maybe they attribute it to something they ate, deem grumpiness derived from a character flaw rather than brash and glaring noise and light. Maybe I like the beers these bars offer because they desensitize me to noise and light. Relative darkness plus recognizable music plus renowned beer momentarily transforms me into a normal person. Maybe I read to concentrate on something silent and motionless and not emitting bursts of light.

Childhood is not where the answer will be found. I'm not about to psychoanalyze myself. Childhood I'll look at through my child's eyes. I'll wait to have a child before I consider my childhood. An unexamined innate sensibility in me issues strong negative feelings when I read writing about childhood that isn't from the point of view of someone much older. Childhood stories by writers in their twenties are the worst for me. They almost always read like young adult stories, stories for teens dressed up as stories for adults, even if they claim to be literary they aren't literary unless they're elaborately literary.

The word *literary* I don't intend to sound like a slur.

Writing about childhood by teens or writers in their twenties mostly comes off as juvenile. Writing about childhood is best by someone much older, who lived it, forgot it, and lives through it again with their own children in a way that jars long-lost memories. Temporal distance reclaims or recovers or reveals the space of childhood.

I will write about childhood in the next decade.

We're outside smoking and England proceeds on autopilot as Lao shivers and smokes two cigarettes in the time we smoke one and I'm thinking that I will write about childhood in the next decade. My writing mind has begun to set out work for the next ten years.

I will write about childhood in the next decade.

It has nothing to do with agents, grants, fellowships, deals.

I will write about childhood in the next decade.

I stepped outside to smoke a cigarette, England suggested he'll do whatever it takes to get something published, Lao interjected and smoked as he listened to England, I thought about fatherhood, and now my work's cut out for the next decade.

I may not write about childhood in the next decade but something generative, productive, ambitious, and enthusiastic leaped ahead a decade, and by doing so marked the present, this moment outside the bar on Bloomsday, as a midpoint between Brooklyn ten years ago and ten years from now when I finish something about childhood spurred by daily contact with a child of our own.

A current goes through me, like what Lao must feel all the time. It's not a fearful shiver, the skin along thighs and forearms constrict and all the little hairs stand on end in anticipation of the next ten years.

How can Gibson give up on that feeling, or was he just taking it all down, starting over, announcing a low point from which things have to get better and he'll rise again?

I don't think there's a way to keep from thinking like this, to keep from translating reality into fiction, no matter if what's written is publishable or not.

Publishability has nothing to do with the little hairs on thighs and forearms standing on end when I think I'll write about childhood in the next decade.

I stood outside this same bar with Lao a year ago and said I'd write something about what it's really like to work for five years in the same office with a changing set of people. All I had at the time was the desire to do it. Which was all I needed to begin it, wanting to write the feeling I had into existence. I didn't have an agenda other than to write something that felt absolutely real.

Rimbaud insisted that *one must be absolutely modern* and it seems to me the way one might be absolutely modern is to dissolve the gap between art and life, dissolve the distance between writer and reader, write something that bridges the gap between writer and reader so there's no frozen sea to split with an ax. This approach, trusting hair on end, anticipating work to come and looking forward to it, is the only way out of this mess of everything back in the bar, everything this Bloomsday is beginning to represent.

Everything's in a state of pre-birth, all these novels ready to live out in the world, ready to take on a life after publication, all these novels ready to live, our child not so far from daily existence outside the womb. Wife said she wasn't sure she could do it. Go through labor, care for the child. Wasn't sure she could do it. I'm not sure I can do it, she said. I said at this point it's not like you have a choice, you're the host environment for a parasite otherwise known as our spawn. The only choice at this point: suicidal homicide of a third trimester fetus or experience as nature intends all the attendant sensations, complemented and supported by the best possible health care afforded by the insurance I secure by going to work every day.

Imagine if all our novels were infants in utero and there was no choice but to bring them into the world, that's what they feel like as they're being finished, as they're rounding out and filling with life and significance and the system of associations among disparate images approaches viability, becomes vital, transforms into something like a living breathing biosphere, an environment rendered in language, something that cannot be stopped, that won't be stopped, a snowball of progressively compounding energy and activity and heat, a steaming boulder of snow on fire rolling downhill. There's no reason the novel when revised and edited and proofed and ready to go cannot then appear on shelves in quality hardback, the writing and editing only half the battle, finding readers more than half the battle for a novel manuscript to become a book.

We always refer to our novel manuscripts as *books*, as though the work in progress were already bound, the way we refer to the infant in utero as a living breathing healthy toddler, an adolescent, a teen. We refer to our novels as books the way everyone refers to our unborn infant as an independent and functional child. It's hopeful, expectant, idealistic if not starry-eyed. We all know our novels will be rejected by agents and editors. We all know our infant in utero will suffer some congenital malady or developmental disorder. We all know life is suffering and yet I can't say I've suffered all my life, so it might be a cosmic set-up, the first half the feel-good section of the movie, for the most part I've felt good, and so it's only natural to expect a rising wave of darkness to crest and break upon my head.

Light and darkness in perpetual round: I've protected myself from darkness by reading and writing, recognizing there's not much time available and while here I'll read and write and walk and read and not so much savor or appreciate the time alive but at least recognize it. All it takes is intermittent recognition, awareness that stalls the churning grinding ever-present spin cycle of existence.

Standing outside finishing this cigarette, world in constant motion, cars down the diagonal avenue across city grid outside the bar accelerating ahead and reversing, accelerating ahead and reversing as fast as they can before accelerating ahead, aware of the whirling dervish world at large.

England's voice blurs and Lao's bouncing, twitching, almost dancing movements blur as he finishes his second cigarette. I'm not sure what season it is, seems like summer but there's a shiver and a rush of streaked vision as I stumble and take a knee.

Lao says you OK there.

England says Throop's down, like I'm a fallen soldier.

I say I'm fine, I'm fine.

I stagger ahead on hands and knees, open palms on sidewalk, knees unused to cement.

I say sorry about that, I'm fine, although I feel like I've been blasted by some beast, like the sidewalk itself, the night, an uncertain future, everything teamed up with the drink to transform into a rush of blood to the head, an uppercut that brought me to my knees.

Lao says ain't nothing a couple pints of water and another beer won't fix right up.

I look forward to the water, want nothing more than to purify myself. It feels less like the beginning of the year than the end, Bloomsday more like New Year's Eve now than New Year's Day. I want a fresh start to write about childhood as we raise our child. A new world is what I want, a new body, a new life built on my old life. It doesn't seem like too much to ask, and now we only have to re-enter the bar to begin it.

XXII.

Lao stops our friendly energetic server and says something in her ear before he mimes the drinking of water. I've grown two feet taller since we stepped outside, or maybe everyone standing near the bar is shorter than when we left. I feel top heavy, like I'm keeping my head aloft an otherwise ethereal body, but I can see at our table Grooms and Feliz chatting and Oates and Gibson and Snare and Lena. We sit at the second booth, the one closer to the barroom and bathroom. We now have two full booths side by side. Snare is still in the same spot, at the opposite end beneath the chalkboard with the beers available on it. He seems slumped over. It's a shame what we do with our time. I have a few pints of water in front of me and they taste like refreshing liquefied mirror glass. I drink a pint and it clarifies the reflection of my soul, not that I say such a thing, I haven't lost my mind. I simply had a vertiginous moment brought on by excessive talk and drink and thought. I was intoxicated not so much by the drink but by what will happen in the next month. In three weeks once the baby comes into our lives the world begins again. I won't care about reading and writing as much as I care about caring for the child. One day soon I might strap the baby into a Baby Björn and take him for a long walk-and-read session, the boy asleep on my chest as I walk sixteen miles from our house through the city and along the river to the Falls Bridge and back home, quietly reading aloud whatever heady European classic I'm reading at the time, re-reading Musil to him, re-reading Mann, re-reading Proust, re-reading Kafka, re-reading Sebald, re-reading Bernhard, re-reading Woolf, re-reading Joyce, re-reading Beckett, re-reading Kis and Schulz and Walser and Zwieg, re-reading Tolstoy, Dostoyevsky, Chekhov, Gogol, Turgenev, re-reading Flaubert, Balzac, Stendhal, re-reading Cervantes, re-reading Bolaño, re-reading Oë, re-reading Kobo Abe, re-reading Handke, re-reading all the Richard and Raymond writers, re-reading Helen DeWitt especially, re-reading Wallace and Auster and Vollmann and Saunders and Franzen and Morrison and Paley and Ishmael Reed and everyone else I haven't thought to re-read, maybe even re-reading Kerouac after more than twenty years away, Melville too, breaking no more ground in terms of acquisition of books, no new literary experiences other than those that advance my son's education, my son sleeping on my chest strapped with his head against my heart as I walk and whisper stories by Hawthorne and Poe, complete novels by DeLillo, Philip Roth, Joseph Roth, Julien Gracq, Georges Perec, Michel Houellebecq, Bret Easton Ellis, Mark Leyner, James Salter, John Updike, re-reading everything for the first time, encountering it all for the first time as the words on the page refract like light through the prism of my voice and enter my son's ears, the rhythms and images saturating my son, the movement putting him to sleep, his infant dreams entangled with language I deem necessary for him to hear.

How am I supposed to concentrate on what Grooms is saying to Oates and Feliz and everyone else, what England and Lao are talking about, what Gibson and Lena are talking about, all this language crisscrossing and improvised and chaotic and drowned by language infiltrating the barroom, the jukebox. The light has taken on an amber glow, like we're submerged in beer, the neon lights on the walls, the wooden decor of a Transylvanian inn afloat on the Baltic Sea, the North Sea, en route through time to some stronghold we'll sack with excessive force in the form of chaotic crisscrossing language, laughter, nods, everyone enjoying themselves so everyone speaks at once except for me and Snare. I'm sipping water so I can order another beer and Snare has stepped through his phone's screen, fit himself through that tight rectangular that dilates as Snare lubricates himself with enough intoxicant to slide inside his smartphone. Tomorrow I really must check to see the damage he did in there, bridges he burned, what explosive devices he improvised while otherwise disengaged.

We all were that way when we were younger, hid from the world thinking we were in it. Snare won't have children and so can remain his own child, whereas Oates and Gibson are fathers. You can see how they relate to everyone. They seem thankful to speak in complete sentences relaying abstract thoughts that don't intend to educate or censure or coo. I will be among them soon, father to a son my wife will deliver in a few weeks if all goes well. She'll deliver a child who will celebrate Bloomsday, the night more than the book that gave the night its name. He'll learn that every night is its own book if he wants it to be. Every night has the *potentiality* of literature. A fine lesson for our unborn son: every night is potential literature, not something to read but to live, a way to see the world and organize clattering echoes into something with "aha!" clarity and laugh as everything falls into place thanks to associative effort more like an effusion of attention, appreciation, recognition of temporary existence on a rocky watery planet.

All life is literature seems like a fine lesson to teach my son, a lesson to replace what had once been religion. Instead of organized religious events to attend on specified holy days his attention will organize reality on a daily basis. Instead of a single ancient sacred book he'll have a secular library of comparatively contemporary literature. It seems like I want to do more than publish novel manuscripts and read published books while walking and whispering to my son. It seems like I want to intuitively improvise an interpenetrating relationship between literature and life that assumes the role of religion.

I wasn't raised particularly religious but have always been interested in religion, the overlapping principles, everything from polytheistic anthropomorphic manifestations the Greco-Romans projected onto sea and thunder and war and wisdom to the monotheistic commonalities of Islam, Christianity, Judaism, to the philosophical guidelines and meditation practices of Hinduism and Buddhism, to the aesthetic mysticism of art and music, to the experiential mysticism of sports and sex and psychedelics, altruism and travel and whatever else triggers the release of the hormone produced by the pituitary gland when a woman is in labor, the hormone produced during orgasm or positive social experience, the hormone that floods the brain during the final instant of consciousness before death, a hormonal surge that heals wounds, produces contentment, reduces anxiety, decreases fear, increases trust, protects against stress, raises levels of empathy, connection, love.

I'm not so much interested in religion as I'm interested in the release of oxytocin. Everything I've done has been geared toward triggering its release to feel its effects. At birth we experience through the placenta our mother's release of oxytocin and forever after we search it out, a similar feeling of peacefulness attained when reading and writing, when walking and reading, when sitting with friends talking and drinking. An inconspicuous army of oxytocin addicts stimulates its release through the act of writing and reading literature. A not particularly elite battalion of soldiers fights an undeclared war against forces impeding oxytocin release, impeding elevated hormonal production that creates a greater sense of commonality, of love, of empathy, all those good terms at the core of the major world religions and most likely common to whatever apparition of consciousness existed elsewhere in the universe that related to the form and spirit of thoughts and the animating force within bodies, human and otherwise.

We are soldiers in the fight against whatever impedes the flow of oxytocin. Without declaring outright war or naming our enemy, we are soldiers in a fight for the souls of unsuspecting civilians who might either promote oxytocin production or impede it through repressive thought, action, behavior, or presence in the world.

I don't want to reduce the world to *us versus them*. It's not so much *us versus them* as some of us who had been civilians were now soldiers who might enlist others to battle it out in favor of oxytocin production. Meanwhile some are civilians and will always be civilians and cannot understand what the hell any of this means. Such civilians won't have read this far anyway, won't have engaged with anything discussed above, won't share what we're interested in here, won't see the world as anything other than a place where they live and work for a time before they die, the world meaningless except for meaning never interrogated or achieved. Meaning always received instead of achieved.

The difference between soldiers and civilians is that we achieve our meaning, actively engage life to transform it into literature, whereas they receive meaning and aren't interested in transforming their experience into anything other than what they think it is, none of which helps us publish our novel manuscripts.

Publishing novel manuscripts seems like it might produce a serious burst of oxytocin. Writing and editing and reading what I've written elevates oxytocin production but not the act of submitting what I write to agents who politely decline to represent me and my work. So the easiest path to publishing my work and experiencing a subsequent burst of seriously elevated amounts of oxytocin may be to win over Grooms, who's already asked for my novel manuscripts and already has them in his email, but I have to win him over so he really wants to promote my writing, the traces of excess oxytocin as it's flowed down the sides of my life.

I've been at the bar longer than anyone other than obliterated Snare. Soon England and Gibson and Oates will go down, the inevitable consequence of time aboard this vessel. I sip water. I need to shake it off. Grooms is here, there he is across the booth and over a bit. He leans forward, pivots at the waist, not slumping forward but with his shoulders square and his torso a straight line, not a curve to it. He leans forward and one might imagine in his lap a number and a degree symbol, maybe 45 degrees. He leans like that to listen to Feliz, the least ambitious among us so maybe he leans toward her because he figures he can take from her without giving in return, can take what she says and remember it and forget it and use it one day instead of feeling obliged to help her.

It's not that I want to give up, I'll never quit, but I want some assurance that something I write might one day be published. Oates has published two novels and he's struggling with his third, the Californian coming-of-age crime novel. He seems to argue that, at this point, of all his grad-school classmates, most have published novels with major presses or respectable small presses. Oates says most of our class has published but they've published *publishable work*, Oates says, a lot of publishable work, my own stuff included, but that only means it's publishable work that's been published. Publication—for most of what's published—is only an indication of an aesthetic midpoint on the pendulum between commercial fiction and unconventional Eastern European metaphysical excellence, a midpoint called conventional contemporary literary fiction. Oates says we all agree that almost all the books his classmates have published have failed to excite readers, failed to do anything other than fill bookstore shelves with at most a two-inch wide spine of product that few will buy and fewer will read and on the whole will be forgotten within a decade by everyone, most likely including the authors and certainly their agents, so I'd caution against taking too much pride in publication alone, considering the fear-driven mentality of the publishing industry is responsible for what's published, and our classmates have been writing for this industry, trying to publish first and foremost. James Salter said the first goal is to publish and the second goal is to write something good. To publish you have to give them the conventional narrative they want, you have to be willing and able to write it too. Some of us are unable to write it, and some of us can write it but aren't willing to write it. I'm not so sure I can anymore and I'm not so sure I'm willing and yet I'm not so sure it matters much anymore because the publishing industry has imploded and there's no way to live off writing novels unless you're one of a handful of anointed talents or lucky hacks. If you're not among the handful there's nothing you can do except write what you want to write how you want to write it without thoughts of publishing via conventional means, or you can quit writing like our friend Gibson.

Lena and Feliz interrupt and ask for clarification from Oates and confirmation from Gibson, who summarizes his stance on the merits of quitting writing. Lena and Feliz shake their heads a lot in all directions, nod yes a lot in unison, and once Gibson's done they try to convince him to reconsider, and Gibson says *GOOD LORD* why does everyone want me to keep at it, do they think if I quit they'll quit too, I don't understand why everyone wants me to write if it brings me no pleasure and no one finds what I write publishable.

Grooms says it's like a death in the family, they don't want to see you give up the ghost, the struggle.

I say if he's not getting adequate release of oxytocin there's no need to bother. (Either no one heard me or no one understood or I didn't actually say this aloud since no one acknowledged it.)

England says we're on this again?

Lao says the last thing the world needs is another writer, the fewer the better. Lao then holds up his pint and suggests we toast again to Gibson giving up the ghost.

We clink glasses and say *hear hear.*

I down some water and request one last *Weihenstephaner Hefeweizen* from our friendly energetic server, since I know where we're going and I will need another lemony-yellow scepter.

Gibson thanks everyone and says he might not write much in the future but he intends to keep reading what we write as it comes out in quality hardcover and paperback, maybe even with French flaps. Even if we self-publish, he'll be there for us as a reader. He says he isn't so much quitting writing as he's devoting himself to reading and living and making the most of the rest of his time alive, and with that he produces a slip of paper from his jeans, spreads it out on the table, and runs it along the edge of the table like a dollar bill he wants to feed into the slot of a change machine. He holds it up and reads "Full many a flower is born to blush unseen," and then he says there's no need to explain that one, I like the rhythm, I think of it more like a fortune cookie, so much of what we work on isn't less beautiful or blushing than what's out in the open, many a flower we write was meant to adorn desk drawers.

We applaud politely and Gibson holds up the slip of paper and tosses it in the air and it comes down in Snare's beer.

Grooms says it's like throwing the garter at a wedding, Snare's beer came down with the quotation so Snare's flower will be the first to bloom in public, and Snare, returned from smartphone immersion, looks up and says I got a toast for ya, and pulls a slip from his pocket and puts a hand over an eye and tries to read it and then says fuck it and stands up best he can in the booth and says you know I didn't know what to think of this guy, this Jonathan David Fuckin' Grooms guy, at first I thought maybe I'd hate him but he's not the worst, a little priggish maybe for my tastes but he's fine by me, and then Snare plops down.

England says that's your quote? Where's that in *Ulysses*?

Snare says all this is *Ulysses* as he sweeps an extended arm to suggest both our tables and everyone in the bar. Snare says all this is the best book of the twentieth century, even if we're a good deal into the twenty-first, the best book is all around us so whatever I say is a quote in it, write it down and put it in the book.

He says it like he knows I'll write it down, in fact it may have been this line that made me think I'd write it down, would get as much of it down as soon as I could. But I wasn't quite thinking about it like that at the time. More so, I was thinking I was surprised Snare made sense even so blotto.

England says he should follow Snare considering how low Snare's set the bar for quotes. England says his quote appeared in the actual book by James Joyce, words you'll find in the text if you Google them or look for them. He says I know this is an obvious quote but someone has to say it. I've been thinking about it, not that I've read all of *Ulysses* of course, just that at Bloomsday these past years whenever someone says this one I think about it, the day after I definitely think about it, so here goes: "History is a nightmare from which I am trying to wake."

England says it as though revealing all faults, all fears, all half-thought suspicions about the world and himself. He says it bashfully, humbly, capitulating, surrendering to forces beyond his control, his ambition to publish and industry indifference. He says it like raising his face to endure steady erosion by the elements. He says the sentence like hoisting a white flag so an era of peace may reign hereafter, and then he sits down and sips his drink and seems satisfied that he said the most famous line in the book, a book he hasn't spent time with for more than a handful of befuddled hours. It doesn't appeal to him and he can't concentrate on it, he doesn't want to write like that any way, but he does like that one famous line early on about trying to wake from the nightmare of history, it liberates him to think about it, and yet I sense his uneasiness with such easily attained freedom.

I wonder if anyone will read the part where Bloom cooks, the most vivid bit, butter in hot pan, cooking kidney. If no one reads that passage this year next year I'll write it out and bring it, if there is a next year. For now, I produce no slip of paper because I know my quotation cold. I say this is what I always say, and every year I think of bringing something different but it's a ritual, it's expected of me, I wouldn't want to disappoint, so I clear my throat and say as slowly as possible "The mouth can be better engaged than with a cylinder of rank weed," and everyone lightly applauds and lightly pounds their pints on the table.

Lao says listen up guys this comes from when Stephen's talking about Shakespeare, animating him to prove that Shakespeare's life was relevant to his contribution to literature, and between descriptions of Shakespeare walking along a river dreaming up Hamlet, associating his dead son Hamnet with Hamlet, associating himself with Hamlet's ghost, and in the middle of Stephen's arguments, he coaches himself, gives himself a pep talk and some literary criticism, he says "Local color. Work in all you know. Make them accomplices." Lao says the librarian argues that the poet's life means nothing next to the poetry of *King Lear*. The poet's drinking and debts mean nothing next to the immortal *King Lear*. The librarian might be totally right, but the bit about working in all you know and making them, whoever they may be, *accomplices*, there's something about these Bloomsdays that make us accomplices to what amounts to a crime against apathy for the written word, so we got to work in some local color, y'all, work in all we know, and make *accomplices* out of everyone who might be on our side, and it's probably also a good time to applaud the presence and participation tonight of our esteemed visitor, Shakespeare's grandfather's ghost himself, influential forefather of all influential figures of the past, none other than the one and only *J. D. Grooms*, who stands and props an elbow on the backs of either booth to either side and says the night's been everything Lao said it might be, Lao did a fantastic job lowering expectations to the point that I figured I'd sip a beer as desperate writer dudes bored the shit out of me, but thankfully that's not been the case, not entirely, Grooms says, and then he says that when listening to the reading earlier today he was struck by the following lines during that weird Q&A section toward the end before Molly Bloom's rhapsodic stream of run-on sentence. It struck me with such percussive force, Grooms says, imprinted itself so powerfully upon my soul that I snagged the nearest copy of the book and found the passage and photographed it to read to you guys later.

Grooms thumbs open his phone and says of all the lines that contribute to this singular novel's outsized reputation *this is the line* that should most resonate with writers today, *this is the line* that should speak to the heart of our work, no matter how divergent our work may be, because within this line there lies the seed of something that can serve us all if we cultivate its instinct, a sentence like a servant we shall call upon whenever we require special inspiration.

Grooms elevates his voice now and projects it so conversations nearby hush as he prepares to share whatever so impressed itself on him and will soon infiltrate us too and trace the contours of our hearts in such a way that minute incisions remain within us for the rest of our lives and leave us vulnerable to weeping if not full-on waterworks.

Grooms lets anticipation hang in the air, he surveys us one by one by one and embodies the role of the great writer, he doesn't just play the role, he *is* the great writer, Jonathan David Grooms, still young, his best work ahead of him. Grooms stands there between the booths like a ship captain, an admiral, governor of an undeclared state, figurehead of a rogue nation encompassed by our booths. He clears his throat and slowly as though intoning what amounts to a gift we will remember and savor as long as we remember his presence tonight, a gift we will pass down as heirlooms of whatever royal family we've improvised these past few years, these past few hours, Grooms delivers what he deems the most pertinent lines of instruction in the novel, lines he's confident will inform our literature and our lives hereafter: "He kissed the plump mellow yellow smellow melons of her rump, on each plump melonous hemisphere, in their mellow yellow furrow, with obscure prolonged provocative melon-smellonous osculation."

Feliz smiles and laughs as we all laugh as Grooms tries to get us to recite the line en masse in time. He stamps his foot like these are the lyrics of an oompah march, but once we make it to "mellow yellow furrow" the song of it shatters on the rocks of the pairing of "obscure" and "prolonged" and instead of forcing it Grooms pockets his phone and raises his glass and leads us in a toast to "obscure prolonged provocative melon-smellonous osculation," although we of course all struggle with "melon-smellonous" at the end.

Oates doesn't miss a beat. He says that Grooms stole the exact line he prepared to read and he shows a handwritten notecard to Grooms who believes Oates for a second and then guffaws as though drunk since it's after midnight on a Saturday night among people who've been drinking since before sunset and so he guffaws as only appropriate.

Oates says he wants to bring in a different line, a line so often overshadowed by the "history's a nightmare" line higher up the page. An inch or two below the nightmare of history line Stephen is asked *what's God?* He pauses to listen and hears the sound of children playing and says "a shout on the street." Oates says it's perfect, so simple, not necessarily a shout on the street, it's anything, at that moment it's *everything*, at that moment when asked what God is Stephen pays attention to the world as it appears to him at that second, he opens his senses, he's as receptive as possible, and he identifies God as what he hears at that moment. The next moment it might have been different of course, it's ideally arbitrary, ecstatically arbitrary, within momentary arbitrariness lies its awesomeness, and then Oates becomes self-conscious and drawls *Hallelujah* and smiles and throws his hands in the air and shakes the spirit loose like a Baptist preacher and raises his glass to "a shout in the street" and we shout "a shout in the street" and listen for a second to what can be heard around us.

Feliz says she loves this, what you guys are doing tonight. This is so great, I wish I had a quotation to share but I'm not much of a Joyce scholar, not that you guys are Joyce scholars either, ha ha ha, but what's so great, the thing is, I like how you're not taking the "best book ever" acclaim all that seriously.

Feliz seems to fumble her subsequent thoughts and dismisses them with a shake of the head and a smile. She raises her glass and toasts the raising of glasses to the idea of the masterpiece, and we raise our glasses and laugh and Grooms says something about it being Lena's turn, so Lena says let's toast to how *fucking hot* Feliz looks tonight and Feliz says let's toast to how hot Lena looks *every* night, and they momentarily act like girls gone wild as we hoot, wonderfully popping the bubble we've blown of literary idiocy, bursting it to great effect with the simple application of faux-bimbo garish poses with tongues out and licking of lips and jacking forearms under breasts and boosting them while puckering and mussing hair.

Lena is the most widely connected younger writer at the table and yet she doesn't read or write the way everyone else reads or writes. She certainly doesn't read canonically. Her stories seem to emerge from hangovers and regret and not quite remembered nights. If all goes well she's on her way to an excellent new story when she begins to recover tomorrow, but I can't think too much about tomorrow, we've entered the home stretch, the final sprint toward last call, or one last drink before last call and the lights come on. Our bill will be several hundred dollars, plates of food have been ordered and devoured and I haven't even noticed them, we must have been outside for an hour, Gibson and Lena polished off sandwiches with fries, someone ordered nachos? I'm not sure what we accomplished this time through, it's not over, the end is yet to come, it'll be a blur, Gibson or Oates will pull an Irish goodbye, under their drained glasses will be twenty dollar bills, it's happened more than once. Lao suggested that Grooms would pay for it all but I don't expect that to happen, I don't want it to happen, I want to pay for it since soon enough I'll be homebound for weeks, months, years as we raise a child, this is my last hurrah, but I shouldn't pay for it with a baby en route and an unemployed wife.

England slides next to Grooms and buddies up to him in a way that seems almost flirtatious although I can't really imagine England doing such a thing, at least not here and now. Grooms seems to appreciate England's invasion of personal space, he even seems to make an effort to slouch with the same degree of shoulder curvature as England. Grooms seems to make an effort to slouch the way most make an effort to sit straight. These two guys across the way, England with his freshly shaven head and Grooms with his high-browed curls, make for a comely conspiratorial duo, a couple of guys speaking in low manly tones that don't cross the table to my ears and then Feliz returns from the bathroom saying *oh my god* I don't think I've ever seen anything like that. I squatted over the toilet and felt like I contracted several communicable diseases.

Gibson asks if it's possible to catch polio from a toilet.

I say what doesn't kill you.

He nods and says I'm going in and a second later he says it seems like Snare mussed the bathroom worse than it was when Feliz was in there. It's true that under the watch of no one other than hidden security cameras and a possible higher power, our friend Snare made his way to the bathroom and emptied contents of stomach and soul upon the toilet entire, the sink, the floor, the walls, somehow even the ceiling, of the tight foul bathroom. Snare's sneakers are smeared in excremental slurry, and it's then that I remember that if I want to forever capture this moment as the evening descends into slop, I can at least secure candid shots of friends in action on Bloomsday, so I remove phone from front pocket of jeans and note that I have exactly *seventeen text messages and three missed calls* from my wife. I nevertheless thumb open the camera app and sit and take some pics and then stand and take more pics including over the shoulder shots of England and Grooms in conspiratorial conversation and Gibson and Oates and Lena and Feliz harmlessly flirting, and then I catch sight of Lao trying to slip out for a solo smoke and so I chase after him and hold two fingers to my lips whereupon he holds up a menthol 100.

I snag it and say oh shit I got all these texts from my wife.

Lao says that's why I ran out here too, to call the wife, and he holds up an old flip phone and presses some buttons and holds it to his ear and moves down the sidewalk saying *hey baby*.

I take a deep minty drag and hold it and exhale and feel like I blow half my intoxicated spirit toward the streetlights, like it sobers me to breathe like that, like I haven't taken a breath since we were last outside to smoke, like I was holding my breath underwater the whole time back in the bar. I look at the texts and voicemails and see and hear that hours ago contractions started and she wants me to come home as soon as I can. She tried to walk over to the bar but turned back once she locked the door when she had a contraction that forced her to sit for a while on our stoop in labor. She made it back inside to the couch waiting for me to come home or at least call and didn't want to call a cab and go to the hospital without me since she trusted I'd be home any second and then the last text said she was going to call the bar but the bar must not have picked up since it's so loud or the bartenders are too busy and that last text was sent minutes ago so I text back *holy shit hang on coming home* and envision wife devising gruesome punishment once everything settles on account of not being home as she went into labor.

I run inside and tell Snare and England and Grooms and Oates and Gibson and Lena and Feliz and our friendly energetic server that my wife is in labor at home and we have to go, I have to go. Everyone says they're coming with me. I don't even begin to think about whether or not they're invited or if it might be better if I don't bring the bar home tonight but there's no time for thought, it's time for action. Remaining drinks are pounded and our friendly energetic server says not to worry about the bill, it's taken care of, and she nods toward Snare who's put the whole thing on his credit card including a generous tip to cover what he did to the bathroom.

Seconds later we're running down the street, England holding a full pint glass he snuck out under his shirt, Grooms holding a whisky high in front of him as though that's the proper way not to spill it, Lao's still on the phone with his wife giving her the play by play saying it's go time for little baby Roebling! and everyone else hurrying in a sprawling stumbling pack behind us. I'm not so much thinking about the child but about my wife's health, thinking also how screwed I'll be for not responding to *seventeen texts and three voice mails*, how this story will make its way to her teetotaling family and I'll be in the doghouse forever even if all goes well from here on out, but I'm not too worried about the drunkenness, the drunkenness seems gone, like all the beer I excrete through my skin as I sweat despite the perfect night as we hurry the few blocks home, half running, chafed inner thighs miraculously cured, leaping curbs, crossing streets where cars wait at stop signs without much concern for right of way or being run over, and then seconds later we're standing on our stoop and rushing inside to a dimly lit room with faux Peruvian flute music on the stereo, something that sounds like synthesized pan flutes, music my wife presented as possible birth music months ago and I said we can at least get real horrific Peruvian flute music or Brian Eno's "Music for Airports" or something minimal like La Neu, but without me home to handle the music selection my wife's on the couch, sweating despite the air-conditioning, knees cocked saying it's too late to go to the hospital, it's too late.

I say we can get there in minutes in a cab.

She says I don't think we have minutes.

I look between her legs and my god she's really dilated and everyone else drunkenly peeks at the tip of my son's head beginning to emerge, *crowning* it's called, there's blood and the whole situation looks like a kitchen sink drain clogged with hair. I kneel beside the couch and hold my wife's hand and press with my thumb into the meat of her hand between thumb and forefinger, a pressure point someone once showed me, a recent father who said all you need to know is *press here* when she's in labor and it will work wonders, and so I press her hand where the new father showed me and it seems to help but who can tell.

Wife lets out a roar, a howl that takes full-body possession as though supersonic wind replaces everything under her skin, a mysterious kaleidoscopic gale surging inside her, and from my vantage on knees beside her on the couch in the front room I can see all the way down our long narrow rowhome as my Bloomsday compatriots make themselves comfortable and admire our wall of floor-to-ceiling bookshelves and back in the kitchen raid the bottles of booze stored in the pantry above the refrigerator, slim pickings at this point left over from our wedding after-party but enough for this hour it seems to England and Snare and Lao, who all take one look at the scene in the front room on the couch and distance themselves from it and as though by muscle memory reach for the bottles and scrounge in the fridge for mixers. I hear them in the kitchen mixing drinks and talking about their novel manuscripts, agents they sent them to, small presses that might be interested, the leads they have, and they seem not to notice that we have all come back to my place not for a little after-party as usual but because my wife is in labor.

Oates and Gibson perch on the stairs for something of an overhead view of the action, Oates filming it on his phone, Gibson asking if we need anything and then he hustles to the kitchen and returns with a cloth napkin wrapped in ice and a glass of water and asks if we need anything else as Oates whispers commentary to his phone as he films, the miracle of birth we're here to witness, emergence of the newest member of the Roebling family. He keeps pausing to say *my god my god this is amazing,* like we're putting on a show, the phone removing him from participation in the scene.

Grooms sits on the part of the sectional couch with a clear view of the action, almost like an impartial obstetrician, an oddly subdued midwife, paring his nails as wife howls and sweats and pushes whenever she feels a contraction. Grooms sits there not averting his eyes, the artist must not avert his eyes, staring it down, taking it in, but ready to act, and during a break between contractions my wife says you're Grooms, nice to meet you, I've heard a lot about you.

Grooms says a pleasure indeed, if there's anything I can do to help I am, well, obviously, sitting right here.

Wife says something about boiling water, isn't someone supposed to boil some water?

Grooms says you certainly don't put a newborn in boiling water, maybe you have the boiling water on hand to dilute stains caused by the afterbirth.

I say that sounds right.

I ask Gibson to run to the little room between the kitchen and the backdoor and find some garbage bags and maybe grab the mop bucket to catch as much of the afterbirth as possible.

Gibson suggests running upstairs for towels and sheets and that sort of thing to cover the couch and I say good idea and Gibson practically hurdles Oates running up the stairs while Lena and Feliz busy themselves browsing our bookshelf, every once in a while looking over into the front room and covering their mouths and doubling over like they can't believe this is happening, which is what I'm thinking too, this can't be happening this way, we'd planned it all out, a cab to the hospital once contractions were four minutes apart and lasted a minute each and went on like that for at least an hour, something like that, the contractions had to be serious enough that wife couldn't speak through them and if there seemed to be decreased fetal movement or if water broke or something else I can't remember we'd go to the hospital's birthing suite area and begin the process of bringing the baby into the world as naturally as possible although we agreed that if she wanted a half-dose or a quarter-dose or even a double dose of an epidural, an overdose of it, who could blame her since even the kicks and hiccups and other little movements the past few weeks caused serious pain. We'd be streaming a documentary and suddenly she'd throw her head back and breathlessly exclaim what sounded like steam released from her body, the baby in her belly like water boiling in a kettle that made her whistle with discomfort, and all along I've had the greatest respect and admiration for the miraculous act of growing this tiny person, a tiny human being person under her tummy skin. I don't know what to do but I assume with everyone here with phones that connect to websites we're in good shape information-wise and Snare could call his wife, who might have some ideas or maybe we just let nature do what it has to do. But what if the cord's wrapped around the baby's neck, if there's massive unexpected bleeding or the heart rate drops, if we need to perform an epistemology.

I know that's not the right word but can't think of the correct pronunciation.

I ask Grooms and he laughs and holds two fingers up and snips them together to suggest a pair of scissors and says you mean an *episiotomy*.

I do not relish the thought of dipping a pair of our sharpest scissors into a bowl of boiling water before snipping my wife's perineum so our baby's head might have an easier time emerging but if I don't do it the baby might go into distress and so I ask Gibson to find the scissors in the top drawer of my desk upstairs and he runs off after them as Oates continues to film, no longer on the stairs but trying to get an artful angle for when more than the crown of the head appears.

Throughout it all I hear voices talking about our books or talking about manuscripts, Snare showing Lao the nonsensical horseshit he posted online, Lao laughing about how he doubts that misremembered misspelled gangsta rap quotations about Snare's eventual supremacy will offend anyone, England telling Lena and Feliz about what he's been working on, everyone standing in front of our wall-sized bookshelf loaded with ninety-percent novels, commenting on different titles, pulling a book down and reading the blurbs on the back or a few lines before exchanging it for another.

I ask them to pull down *The Great Wall of China* and read the short title story aloud to distract us, but instead I hear someone say *oh man I love this one* or *have you read this one*, as though the books on our shelves matter.

I whisper into my wife's ear that all that matters is making sure that our first-born and possibly only son makes it safely into the world, all those hours walking and reading and writing and then drinking while talking about writing and reading and caring about all this stuff to the extent that daydreams involve considering myself a literary fundamentalist foot soldier in some undeclared war for the souls of the citizens of the country, all of it I'd exchange in a second for knowledge that wife and newborn survive this night and thrive thereafter, all because I've been celebrating Bloomsday, celebrating the idea of the masterpiece more than the masterpiece itself, choosing to spend the night with writer reader drinker friends and Grooms on the real first day of the year instead of sitting at home on the couch with the wife ready to escort her to the hospital when time comes to go. Now here we are with towels and garbage bags replacing old issues of the local free weekly newspaper she spread under herself to protect the couch, towels and garbage bags all around now to protect from splashing, Jonathan David Grooms sitting not five feet away, not instructing us or saying much at all, almost seeming sleepy in fact, observing, moved by the spectacle of it, and every once in a while someone from the kitchen and middle room, Lao or Snare or England or Lena or Feliz, comes to the front room and asks how it's going and Gibson greets them and turns them back to the middle room with the bookshelves or to the kitchen, asks if they'd like a drink and pours them a screwdriver cut with seltzer, before he returns to his spot in the front room, vigilant and engaged in a way he no longer finds through writing, although something about his sense of purpose makes me think he isn't done, he'll write about this night or the night will make him want to write in general. He needs something to write about that writes itself.

Grooms on the couch disappears into himself as he watches my wife in the throes of another contraction. He seems absent in a way that makes me think he's witnessing the evening with total detached concentration, the organic version of what Oates does with his phone. I'm doing it too as I sit there holding my wife's hand, pressing down with thumb as though it helps, talking to her, encouraging her to keep at it, it's almost over, we're almost there, every minute we're closer to the end, every second closer to the end, always closer to the moment it's over, we're almost there, dive into it, feel it, I'm saying, really feel it, surrender to it, submit.

I say this sort of thing based on something I read about surrendering to the pain, although I can't imagine what it feels like to have a tiny human work its way out of me. I've joked that I've had extreme bowel movements that surely weighed more than eight pounds expelled from a much smaller orifice, so I know *exactly* what it's like to give birth, although of course my excrement wasn't alive or squirmy or liable to stop breathing any minute.

Grooms looks at us with eyes half-mast like he's meditating more than anything else. I realize he's writing in a way, preparing himself to write about this. Oates is recording this to write about it, Gibson is doing everything he can to help and will write about this, or possibly no one will write about it directly, it won't appear like this exactly, but everyone will soon incorporate a home birth into their fiction and it's then I decide that as soon as I can, as soon as I find the time once things settle with the kid, even before that happens, right away, the next morning once I have some coffee I will start to tell the story of this night. I want to write something that writes itself, that bursts from me alive like this. The first thoughts I have as my wife is in labor and I hold her hand is I want to get this down, the whole night, Grooms, all of it, from the very beginning, before it began, when I first received the message about where and when we'd gather to celebrate the one hundred and eighth anniversary of Bloomsday. I want to commemorate it and get it all down before I forget it, before Grooms writes it, before Oates writes it, before Gibson writes it, before Snare writes it, before Lao writes it, before England writes it, before Lena writes it, before Feliz writes it, I want to write it exactly as it happened without exaggeration.

We celebrate the idea of the masterpiece more than the masterpiece itself and cap the night with the arrival of this masterpiece of a little man, this utterly perfect little man about to emerge from my wife, who's holding up, enduring it, undergoing it like an athletic event, panting, breathing hard, sweating, groaning, really exerting but doing fine it seems, not in too much distress, and then Grooms's eyes open wide and Gibson emotes and everyone in the other room hurries to the front room and Oates slides around and kneels at Grooms's feet for a good filming angle and I kneel on the couch and touch for the first time the extraordinarily unclean head of my child and ease the bloody slimy bluish purplish glory out as everyone cheers and coaches me and time and space collapse as I wipe the baby off with a moist dish cloth Gibson gives me and I put the baby on my wife's chest as my wife cries and laughs and coos and the baby cries and I'm laughing and Grooms says it doesn't look like a son, Gibson and Oates also say I don't think it's a boy, and Lao comes in and pats me on the back and says *congratulations*, you're the daddy of a beautiful little baby girl, and I whoop and say to my wife *it's a girl, it's a girl, it's a girl*, and she laughs and says *a girl of course, of course it's a girl*, and I say of course, of course, how could it be anything other than a girl, of course, *yes*, and everyone applauds and whoops and Gibson hands me the scissors and says he's done a quick search and it's safe to cut it and tie the ends for now, it'll fall off naturally or it can be stitched when we go to the hospital, and so I try to cut the cord but the first snip doesn't cut all the way through so I press harder on the scissors like slicing through the tough sinew of a rotisserie chicken, and now the cord is cut and blood flows from it that we direct into the bucket and then once the blood slows we tie the cord and I say we should go to the hospital and make sure everything's fine, so everyone leaves the house as wife and I and little baby girl strapped in a car seat get in a cab and Gibson and Oates head back to the bar to retrieve their bikes while Grooms and Lao and Snare and Lena and Feliz start toward England's place to complete an evening that's already lasted until dawn.

On the seventeenth of June the sky lightens around four in the morning. Days will lengthen for less than a week before they'll shorten as I work on this and sit with our tiny daughter we almost name Molly before we decide to call her *Bloom*—it's not my idea but my wife's—and when I think about everything we've been through, everything to come, lives now over as we've known them, new lives finally and officially begun, I ask myself if I can imagine calling her *Bloomy* or *Bloomer* or *Bloomster*, a blossoming blooming little baby girl, and I say *yes, yes, hands down I will yes*, and a few days later, as soon as I get a chance, I start writing a story to one day whisper in her ear about the night she plunged headfirst into the world.

Lee Klein is the author of *Chaotic Good* (Sagging Meniscus), *Neutral Evil)))* (SM), *JRZDVLZ* (SM), *The Shimmering Go-Between* (Atticus Books), *Incidents of Egotourism in the Temporary World* (Better Non Sequitor), and *Thanks + Sorry + Good Luck: Rejection Letters from the Eyeshot Outbox* (Barrelhouse Books). His translation of Horacio Castellanos Moya's *Revulsion: Thomas Bernhard in San Salvador* (New Directions) received a 2015 PEN/Heim Translation Fund Award. He lives in the Philadelphia area with his wife and daughter. Visit litfunforever.com for more.

www.ingramcontent.com/pod-product-compliance
Lightning Source LLC
Chambersburg PA
CBHW021401270125
20918CB00013B/718